7/30/59

D1575662

REASON AND CHANCE
IN SCIENTIFIC DISCOVERY

Reason and Chance
in Scientific Discovery

R. TATON

Translated by A. J. Pomerans

HUTCHINSON
SCIENTIFIC AND TECHNICAL
LONDON

HUTCHINSON & CO. (*Publishers*) LTD
178–202 Great Portland Street, London, W.1

London Melbourne Sydney
Auckland Bombay Toronto
Johannesburg New York

★

First published 1957

*Set in twelve point Bembo, one point
leaded, and printed in Great Britain
by The Anchor Press, Ltd.,
Tiptree, Essex*

CONTENTS

PLATES

PREFACE

All scientific progress is the result of a chain of discoveries of differing degrees of importance and significance. Each of these discoveries, while based more or less directly on previous work, leads in turn to new advances. This forward march, however, is far from being regular. Its general sense is often obscured during periods of relative stagnation or even of apparent regression. At other times, again, scientific progress seems to be accelerated, producing vast changes in a whole realm of science, or creating fruitful connections between different sectors of our knowledge.

In fact all discoveries in Science appear to have different aspects depending on their domain (i.e. mathematics, theory or experiment), on the temperament, the background and the previous contributions of their author, and on the nature of the external circumstances under which the discovery is made.

The making of a discovery presupposes in the discoverer undeniable qualities of scientific procedure and of intuition, and even a quite special genius when it comes to questions of important syntheses and of audacious theories. Every discovery of any importance will, at the outset, encounter very strong resistances, and to engage in the unavoidable struggle against routine and prejudice a scientist must have unquestionable intellectual courage. If, in this struggle, he should become somewhat isolated, he is nevertheless linked with those who came before him and with his contemporaries. In effect, the science of an epoch is the result of the successive contributions of many generations of research workers, be they geniuses or only simple and unknown servants of science. In its presentation, its objectives and in its applications, science always reflects the current preoccupations of civilization.

The study of the origins, the conditions, the circumstances, and the character of scientific discovery involves widely varying epistemological and psychological aspects, and many studies, often reaching different conclusions, have been devoted to it. In order to

avoid the dangerous territory of interpretations that are too systematic, I have chosen to do no more than give a description of the
different realms of scientific discovery, its principal factors and its
essential aspects, with examples drawn from the various fields.
In order not to lower their illustrative value I have tried to relate
my examples in the most objective way, avoiding all convenient
schematizations which give nothing but a distorted image of what is
always a very complex reality.

Because of this, my conclusions will often appear less clear-
cut and less categorical than those of certain other authors; but are
not the very complex aspects of all discoveries in themselves a faithful reflection of the variety of temperaments and the diversity of
circumstances?

PART ONE

The Different Realms of Discovery

INTRODUCTORY REMARKS

SCIENTIFIC creation, i.e. discovery, appears in different forms which often depend on the particular scientific realm to which they belong. Such realms are mathematics, theoretical science, experimental science and observation.

The logical deductions of the mathematicians, the attempts at interpretation and synthesis of the theoretician, the special techniques of the observer and of the experimenter do, in fact, require very different research conditions, which will be discussed in the following chapter. In the meantime, a careful study of the circumstances and of the different stages of creative work will reveal that these differences are actually not at all as deep as they appear to be at the beginning.

Thus it comes about that a good many of the remarks and observations on mathematical research can be applied in only slightly differing form to other types of research, and this will allow us to make a more rapid analysis. At the start, this general study must not be considered as anything but a long introduction, the conclusions of which will be confirmed, completed or illustrated by the examples that are analysed in subsequent chapters.[1]

---

[1] Far from wishing to develop a thesis on the nature and the origins of discoveries or of scientific inventions in this essay, I shall merely show the various and sometimes contradictory forms of these essential manifestations of scientific activity. The examples which I have chosen to illustrate each one of these forms will therefore be presented in their full complexity. Owing to this, the principal source of documentation is the evidence of scientists (for example that of Poincaré in *Science et Méthode* and in *La Valeur de la Science*; that of J. Hadamard, L. de Broglie, E. Bauer, in the notes of the sessions of the *IXe Semaine Internationale de Synthèse: L'Invention*, Paris, Alcan, 1938, that of Charles Nicolle in his *Biologie de l'Invention* and in the statements of discoverers and of their contemporaries). More detailed references will be given in the course of the work, particularly with respect to the philosophical studies dedicated to the problem of invention and of scientific discovery. The construction of this work is such that it is not necessary to cite them in this preliminary note.

Finally it must be noted that the complexity of the subject, and the small compass of this work, make it necessary that this essay be presented more as an assembly of commentaries than as an ambitious attempt at synthesis.

CHAPTER I

MATHEMATICS

THE realm of mathematical invention is probably the one that has most seriously been investigated. The first investigation was made in 1905 in *L'Intermédiaire des Mathématiciens* on the somewhat secondary question of the 'mathematical dream', i.e. on the possible existence of cases in which problems vaguely studied in the waking state were solved in a subsequent dream. The answers showed that even if this phenomenon could occur, it was at least very exceptional. Most correspondents emphasized that a solution appeared at the very moment of waking. This is a typical example of mathematical inspiration manifesting itself at moments during which no active research is taking place, and which we shall encounter later on in the most varying forms.

Very shortly after this first enquiry, a second, much vaster and more general, was launched by *L'Enseignement mathématique*.[1] Because of the number and preciseness of the questions asked, and the number of replies which they elicited, and also because of the very rational methods employed by the mathematicians and psychologists charged with examining and interpreting them, this was a most valuable enquiry. Unfortunately, as happens so frequently in an undertaking of this kind, the replies came mostly from second-class research workers, while the majority of mathematicians of first rank did not bother to reply to the very precise questions put to them by the investigators. Nevertheless, some time later the greatest mathematician of the time, Henri Poincaré, in the course of a now famous lecture,[2] produced evidence of altogether exceptional interest on the conditions of mathematical discovery.

---

[1] The questionnaire was published in Volumes IV and VI (1902 to 1904) of that journal, and the results of the enquiry were given in Volumes VI to X (1904 to 1908).

[2] '*L'invention mathématique*', a lecture delivered on the 23rd May, 1908, to the General Institute of Psychology of Paris, published in *L'Enseignement mathématique*, Vol. X, 1908, and in *Science et Méthode*, Paris, Flammarion, 1908, and later in *Science and Method*, translated by Francis Maitland, Nelson, 1914.

THE EVIDENCE OF HENRI POINCARÉ

Poincaré's elegant article on mathematical invention deserves to be quoted in full. In it, the author begins by stressing the great importance of making a deep study of the processes of mathematical invention.[1]

'The genesis of mathematical discovery is a problem which must inspire the psychologist with the keenest interest. For this is the process in which the human mind seems to borrow least from the exterior world in which it acts or appears to act only by itself and on itself, so that by studying the process of geometric thought we may hope to arrive at what is most essential in the human mind.'

After pointing out that his personal observations are not in entire agreement with the conclusions of the enquiry carried out by *L'Enseignement mathématique*, he immediately comments on lack of comprehension and on error in mathematics, attributing the latter to the imperfection of our memory, which sometimes uses inexact propositions. Nevertheless he also opposes the idea that a special mathematical aptitude can be reduced to a particularly good memory or to prodigious powers of attention.

Noting that mathematicians are only rarely good calculators or excellent chess-players, Poincaré gives an account of his personal memory which leads to most interesting general reflections on the processes of mathematical creation:

'As for myself I must confess that I am absolutely incapable of doing an addition sum without a mistake. Similarly I should be a very bad chess-player. I could easily calculate that by playing in a certain way I should be exposed to such and such a danger. I should then review many other moves which I should reject for other reasons, and I should end by making the move I first examined, having forgotten in the interval the danger I had foreseen.

'In a word my memory is not bad but it would be insufficient to make me a good chess-player. Why then does it not fail me in a difficult mathematical argument in which the majority of chess-players would be lost? Clearly because it is guided by the general trend of the argument. A mathematical demonstration is not a simple juxtaposition of syllogisms; it consists of syllogisms *placed in a certain*

[1] *Science and Method, op. cit.*

order, and the order in which these elements are placed is much more important than the elements themselves. If I have the feeling, so to speak, the intuition of this order, so that I can perceive the whole of the argument at a glance, I need no longer be afraid of forgetting one of the elements; each of them will place itself naturally into the position prepared for it, without my having to make any effort of memory.

'It seems to me then, as I repeat an argument I have learnt, that I could have discovered it. This is often only an illusion but even then, even if I am not clever enough to create for myself, I rediscover it myself as I repeat it.

'We can understand that this feeling, this intuition of a mathematical order which enables us to guess the hidden harmonies and relations, cannot belong to everyone.'

After having noted that owing to this fact most minds cannot grasp even the first steps of higher mathematics, and that others again, while understanding and applying mathematics, are unable to create, Poincaré distinguishes creative minds in the following words:

'Lastly, others possess the special intuition I have spoken of, more or less highly developed, and they can not only understand mathematics, even though their memory is in no way extraordinary, but they can become creators, and seek to make discoveries with more or less chance of success according as their intuition is more or less developed.'

Then follows his famous definition of mathematical discovery:

'What, in fact, is mathematical discovery? It does not consist in making new combinations with mathematical entities already known. That can be done by anyone and the combinations that could be so formed would be infinite in number and the greater part of them would be absolutely devoid of interest. Discovery consists precisely in not constructing useless combinations but in constructing those that are useful, which are an infinitely small minority. Discovery is discernment, selection.'

Poincaré then remarks that those mathematical facts are worth studying which reveal 'unsuspected relationships between other facts long since known', but from the immense number of combinations of which, 'borrowed from widely separated domains' as they are, the inventor unconsciously and effortlessly excludes the majority of unfruitful combinations.

'Unfruitful combinations do not so much as present themselves to the mind of the discoverer. In the field of his consciousness there never appear any but useful combinations and some that he rejects, which, however, partake to some extent of the character of fruitful combinations. Everything happens as if the discoverer were a secondary examiner, who had only to interrogate candidates declared eligible after passing a preliminary test.'

In order to 'penetrate further and to see what happens in the very soul of the mathematician' Poincaré then passes from these general reflections, suggested to him by the work of other geometers, to some personal memories, i.e. to describing the circumstances in which he made his first discoveries in connection with Fuchsian functions. This description has been quoted so often that it has almost become classical. Nevertheless because of the very penetrating introspective method that it illustrates, and also because of the precision with which the train of thought has been reconstructed, it is of such exceptional interest that it must be repeated here. But first we must describe the background which will allow us to assess the importance of those fundamental discoveries which, at a stroke, made the name of the young mathematician.

THE DISCOVERY OF FUCHSIAN FUNCTIONS

Henri Poincaré was then at the beginning of his scientific career. A young lecturer in mathematical analysis at the Faculty of Science at Caen, he had not yet published anything apart from his thesis on the theory of partial differential equations, and some notes that did not fully reflect his mathematical genius.

The theory of functions of a complex variable, which was first propounded in about 1802, has since been remarkably fruitful in the domain of infinitesimal analysis. Thus the theory of elliptic and of Abelian functions has led to the integration of all algebraic functions. In the construction of these elegant theories an essential part was played by a remarkable property of elliptic functions: their double periodicity in the complex plane—i.e. the fact that these uniform functions assume two distinct periods ω and ω', the ratio of which is a complex number, and which thus repeatedly assume the same values at the homologous points of a series of equal parallelograms, covering the entire complex plane without any gaps or overlaps. This property of double periodicity of elliptic functions contributed to important theories and made it an object of admiration for all mathematicians. However, it could not then be applied to new theories. Poincaré's great merit in his fundamental discovery of Fuchsian functions lay not so much in perfecting the detail, as in daring to conceive of these functions in the first place.

He was interested in the remarkable but limited work of the German mathematician Lazarus Fuchs (1833–1902) on differential equations of the second order with algebraic coefficients, in Hermite's theory of modular functions and also in the inversion of the hypergeometric series studied by Schwartz. While the first of these works led him to attempt the much more difficult solution of linear differential equations with algebraic coefficients of any order, the two other studies suggested to him the possibility of a daring extension of the notion of periodicity. Appreciating the essential part that groups of discontinuous transformation played in this study, he studied the groups of linear transformations of the form

$$u_1 = \frac{au + b}{cu + d}$$ (a, b, c, d, constants) and determined those amongst

them corresponding to a 'polygonal generator'. These polygons are curvilinear figures bounded by arcs of circles and derived from one another by transformations of the group, and covering the interior of the circle without gap or overlap (case of Fuchsian functions). The ingenious use of a non-Euclidean geometric picture allowed him, while proving the legitimacy of this geometry, to show the necessary and sufficient conditions which ought to be satisfied by a group of the desired type. He then determined the invariable meromorphic functions, invariant under the transformations of such a group; these functions, which he called 'Fuchsian' as a tribute to the mathematical Fuchs whose works had introduced him to this study, soon led to the solution of the problem itself and also to a number of other results of the greatest importance. Thus he discovered that two Fuchsian functions belonging to the same group are related algebraically, and that conversely the co-ordinates of a point on any algebraic curve can be expressed by Fuchsian functions with the same parameter. At the same time he showed that the

general integral of differential linear equations with algebraic coefficients is obtained by means of functions generalizing Fuchsian functions, i.e. Zeta (Fuchsian) functions, and he studied the case of real integrals of differential equations of this type with real co-efficients. Furthermore, he obtained very important results on qualitative integration in his studies of singular points, limit cycles and periodic integrals.

One cannot help admiring Poincaré's courage and genius. He was not afraid of even the most far-reaching generalization and, with rare facility, seized and brought together opportunities which the most diverse branches of mathematics offer to a universal mind such as his. All the results obtained in the course of these first studies were to reappear in his later work, devoted to the most diverse sectors of mathematics, to celestial mechanics and to mathematical physics. Speaking of his work Camille Jordan wrote: 'It is beyond ordinary praise, and forcefully recalls what Jacobi wrote of Abel: that he had solved problems which before him nobody would even have dared to pose.'

His nephew, Pierre Boutroux, the mathematician and historian of science, said of him:

'Instead of following a straight path, his mind radiated from the centre of a problem to the periphery.

'He always neglected details and heeded nothing but the essentials, which he covered with amazing rapidity; the facts he discovered ranged themselves around their centre spontaneously, and were instantly and automatically sorted in his memory.'

These few remarks on the scope of the discovery of Fuchsian functions, and on the exceptional character of Poincaré's genius, justify our stressing the importance of his accurate and informative evidence on the origins and circumstances of his discovery. Its exceptional importance lies not only in the light it throws on the genesis of a discovery, but also on the creative processes of an exceptional mind.

THE ACCOUNT OF THE DISCOVERY

'For a fortnight,' he writes,[1] 'I had been attempting to prove that there could not be any functions analogous to what I have

---

[1] *Science and Method, op. cit.*

since called Fuchsian functions. I was, at that time, very ignorant. Every day I sat down at my table and spent an hour or two trying a great number of combinations and arrived at no result. One night I took some black coffee, contrary to my custom, and was unable to sleep. A host of ideas kept surging in my head; I could almost feel them jostling one another, until two of them coalesced, so to speak, to form a stable combination. When morning came I had established the existence of one class of Fuchsian functions, those that are derived from the hypergeometric series. I had only to verify the results, which only took a few hours.

'Then I wished to represent these functions by the quotient of two series. This idea was perfectly conscious and deliberate; I was guided by the analogy with elliptical functions. I asked myself what must be the properties of these series, if they existed, and I succeeded without difficulty in forming the series which I have called Theta-Fuchsian.

'At this moment I left Caen where I was then living, in order to take part in a geological conference arranged by the School of Mines. The incidents of the journey made me forget my work. When we arrived at Coutances, we got into a brake to go for a drive, and, just as I put my foot on the step, the idea came to me, though nothing in my former thoughts seemed to have prepared me for it; that the transformations I have used to define the Fuchsian functions were identical with those of non-Euclidean geometry. I made no verification and had not time to do so, since I took up the conversation again as soon as I had sat down in the brake, but I felt absolute certainty at once. When I got back to Caen I verified the result at my leisure to satisfy my conscience.

'I then began to study arithmetical questions without any great apparent result and without suspecting that they could have the least connexion with my previous researches. Disgusted at my want of success I went away to spend a few days at the seaside and thought of entirely different things. One day as I was walking on the cliff, the idea came to me, again with the same characteristics of conciseness, suddenness and immediate certainty, that arithmetical transformations of ternary indefinite quadratic forms are identical with those of non-Euclidean geometry.

'Returning to Caen I reflected on this result and deduced its consequences. The example of quadratic forms showed me that there are Fuchsian groups other than those which correspond with the hypergeometric series. I saw that I could apply to them the theory of the Theta-Fuchsian series and that, consequently, there are Fuchsian functions other than those which are derived from the hypergeometric series, the only ones I knew up to that time. Naturally I proposed to form all these functions. I laid siege to them systematically and captured all the outworks one after the other. There was one, however, which still held out, whose fall would carry with it that of the central fortress. But all my efforts were of no avail at first, except to make me better understand the difficulty, which was already something. All this work was perfectly conscious.

'Thereupon I left for Mont Valérien where I had to serve my time in the army, and where my mind was preoccupied with very different matters. One day as I was crossing the street the solution of the difficulty which had brought me to a standstill came to me all at once. I did not try to fathom it immediately, and it was only after my service was finished that I returned to the question. I had all the elements and had only to assemble and arrange them. Accordingly I composed my definitive treatise at a sitting and without any difficulty.'

THE ROLE OF THE SUBCONSCIOUS

Poincaré leaves it at this simple example, but states that he could make similar remarks on his other research work. In his account he notes that it is the 'appearance of sudden illuminations obvious indications of a long course of previous work' which strike us with peculiar force. In this he sees an almost general rule.

'Often, when a man is working at a difficult question, he accomplishes nothing the first time he returns to work. Then he takes more or less of a rest and sits down again at his table. During the first half hour he still finds nothing, and then, all at once the decisive idea presents itself to his mind. We might say that the conscious work proved more fruitful because it was interrupted, and the rest has restored force and freshness to the mind. But it is more probable that the rest was occupied with unconscious work, and that the results of this work was afterwards revealed to the geometrician, exactly as in the cases I have quoted, except that the revelation, instead of coming to light during a walk or a journey, came during a period of conscious work, but independently of this work, which at most only performs the unlocking process, as if it were the spur that excited into conscious form the results already acquired during the rest, which till then remained unconscious.'[1]

Poincaré ascribes the sudden appearance of inspiration to the working of the unconscious; it invariably follows on days of apparently unfruitful work and later periods of apparent rest, during which the unconscious arranges the results of previous periods of work of which the conscious mind is no longer aware. Inspiration, accompanied by a sense of absolute certainty and unsupported by any full demonstration, must, in its turn, be followed by a period of conscious work when the mind must implement the inspiration, deduce and order its immediate consequences, arrange a proof, and above all verify the results.

In this unconscious operation, which generally chooses from all possible combinations only those which will lead to a fruitful result, Poincaré sees the influence of 'some aesthetic sensibility; a feeling for mathematical beauty, for the harmony of number and forms, and for geometrical elegance'.

'The useful combinations,' he adds, 'are precisely the most beautiful, I mean those that can most charm that special sensibility that all mathematicians know, but of which laymen are so ignorant that they are often tempted to smile at it.'[2]

This description and interpretation of creative effort by the author of so many essential discoveries bearing upon the most varied branches of the deductive sciences, viz. mathematics, celestial mechanics and mathematical physics, is perhaps the most penetrating attempt by any discoverer to explain the genesis of his discoveries. His conclusions can only be applied in full to those domains of science in which observations and experiments play no more than a very indirect role, but some of them, particularly the interpretation of sudden inspiration and the stress on the role of unconscious work, will be found to have bearing on our later study of other aspects of scientific discovery.

But for the moment, in looking at mathematics and the allied

[1] *Op. cit.*
[2] *Op. cit.*

sciences, we shall cite further evidence which, while not contradicting and often confirming that of Poincaré, nevertheless will draw our attention to other essential points.

THE ROLE OF OBSERVATION

We shall first cite the instance of the mathematician Charles Hermite (1822–1901), a very talented analyst, a remarkable teacher and one of the principal leaders of the French mathematical school at the end of the nineteenth and the beginning of the twentieth century. Hermite was the first to demonstrate the transcendental nature of e, the number commonly used in analysis. He was a born analyst and his mind preferred abstractions to the concrete images that other mathematicians find so useful. 'His eyes,' wrote Poincaré, 'seemed to flee from contact with the world; it was not outside, but inside himself, that he sought visions of truth.'[1] Hermite considered it very difficult, particularly in mathematics, to reconstruct the mystery of a discovery, since that series of transitions in which one could recognize the real path taken by research appeared very rarely in the final proof. 'Nevertheless,' he added, 'regarding the intellectual processes of geometers, we may make the very simple remark that, in it, observation has an important place and plays a great role.'[2]

In support of this contention, Hermite quotes a few examples from one of the most abstract branches of mathematics, the theory of numbers, viz. the periodicity of the development in continuous fractions of the roots of an equation of the second degree with commensurable coefficients, the law of quadratic (or cubic) reciprocals, the approximate expression of the number of prime numbers lower than a given limit, the proof that there is an infinite number of primes, etc. Particularly with regard to the last example he showed that if one supposed that there was a finite number of primes, the observation of a very simple fact of divisibility shows a contradiction, which lends weight to the argument leading to the classic demonstration of the infinity of that series.

Hermite's observation is an important complement to Poincaré's remarks. In mathematics, as in other sciences, a number of important

---

[1] *La Valeur de la Science*, Paris, Flammarion, 1913.
[2] *Œuvres de Charles Hermite*, Vol. IV, Paris, 1917.

discoveries arise from the observation of a previously unnoticed and isolated fact, the exception to what was previously considered to be a rule, the discovery of an error, a gap or fault in a proof, the observation of a new property in a particular case, etc. While Poincaré mainly emphasized the efforts of the research worker embarking on a chosen course, Hermite showed the principal ways in which this choice operates.

THE CHOICE OF SUBJECT

It must, however, not be overlooked that this choice depends also on the personality of the research worker, on his preferences for a particular scientific subject and approach and also on the fact that he is influenced and even restricted by the profound nature of the problems. In a very short but most thoughtful passage, M. Jacques Hadamard shows the interaction of these two influences:

'If every creator naturally stamps his work with his own personality, in science this tendency is counteracted by an opposite tendency, that of objectivity.

'In mathematics we are servants rather than masters, Hermite once said to me. Generally speaking and to a varying extent, scientists follow their temperaments in their choice of problems. This is the way of the average mathematician.'[1]

But there are exceptions, and that of Henri Poincaré is particularly striking:

'The average research worker, but not Poincaré. He did not pursue a subject because of his mental resourcefulness, but because of the needs of science. They were the starting points of his thoughts. Somehow these arose outside himself, and a "superior force" struck a light in him which he then passed on to the world.'[2]

This judgement, together with Hermite's preceding remarks, allows us to get a better idea of the origins of most mathematical discoveries. For the 'average research worker', for the worthy mathematicians of which every epoch sees a great many, the subject of their research is dictated by observations made in their chosen field which lead them either towards a deeper understanding of a detail, the subsequent development of a theory, or even towards

[1] J. Hadamard, 'The Centenary of Henri Poincaré' (*Rev. Hist. Sc.*, VII, 1954).
[2] *Ibid.*

attempting the reconstruction of a whole branch. But for a mathematician of Poincaré's stature, it is the needs of science that somehow dictate to him the subject of his research, that tempt him to revise entire fields or at least to develop them to the point of satisfying new needs, or yet to adapt other domains with which they had previously been quite unconnected. At this level the influence of the discoverer's taste is discernible only in the general trend of his work, but certainly not in the choice of a particular topic for research. His breadth of vision permits him to span, in the one study, domains of science that are very far removed, and to envisage new syntheses affecting science as a whole.

The great contemporary mathematician Jacques Hadamard, some of whose remarks have already been quoted, is one who takes a very keen interest in the problem of mathematical invention; the various articles which he has devoted to this subject, his very brilliant communication to the *IXe Semaine Internationale de Synthèse*[1] and his important work on the psychology of invention[2] contain many highly important reflections and exact details on this fundamental subject. We shall return to M. Hadamard's acute observations on the role of error in certain discoveries and to his explanations of some very paradoxical failures since, in a similar form, his observations can be applied to quite different aspects of scientific discovery.

As regards mathematical invention in particular, M. Hadamard accepts completely Poincaré's ideas on the fundamental part that the subconscious plays in the work of discovery, but he completes the description of the research workers' efforts with some remarks that illustrate certain aspects with particular clarity.

One of the particular characteristics of mathematics is the fact that in it invention starts from the very moment that a pupil is confronted with a problem that he has to solve. Evidently this is a case of a minor effort of invention in which the subject is set in advance, and where the anticipated result should lead to no new elements. But although this is not a discovery in the proper sense of the word, the pupil must nevertheless attempt a discovery in so far

---

[1] '*L'Invention scientifique—La mathématique*', in *L'Invention IXe Semaine Internat. de Synthèse*, Paris, Alcan, 1938.
[2] *An Essay on the Psychology of Invention in the Mathematical Field.* Dover Publications Inc., 1954.

as he has to produce rigorous arguments permitting him to pass from known elements to the proposition to be proved or demonstrated, or to the solution to be determined. If the pupil ignores the actual questions that are asked, but would rather make original remarks on the problem that he has to solve or if, still better, he himself poses the problems, then his work can no longer be distinguished from that of the creative mathematician, except by degree. The very fact of posing problems is a sign of an interest in research and a curiosity of mind, which are but some of the fundamental qualities characteristic of the creative mathematician.

MATHEMATICAL APTITUDE

The question of mathematical aptitude has been the subject of investigation on the part of many psychologists. Poincaré, in the text already quoted, very properly distinguishes three principal types of mind: those who cannot understand even the first steps of higher mathematics, those who, by an act of memory and by sufficient reflection, can follow any mathematical reasoning, and finally those creative minds who not only understand but who actively further the advance of a particular field.

For greater precision, in the last type we should also distinguish between mathematicians who by sustained and methodical effort can perfect an already existing theory, or contribute new results of varying importance to well-defined branches, and those truly creative minds who can devise new theories and conceptions, and whose influence can be felt in many fields.

The vast number of all those who have participated in the progress of mathematics ranges from such geniuses as Archimedes, Fermat, Newton, Leibniz, Euler, Lagrange, Gauss, Galois, Abel, Riemann, Weierstrass, Cantor and Poincaré, to those modest craftsmen who, by assiduous work, may have discovered some new detail.

In various degrees and different forms, all these scientists undoubtedly have a common gift and a special aptitude for mathematics, but this gift appears under very different guises. Thus, M. Hadamard says that there is no unique mathematical aptitude; there are various kinds of mathematical brains which differ considerably from one another.

Different psychologists have, nevertheless, tried if not to explain this 'gift', at least to discover its origin.

We need only mention the phrenological theory of Gall, which, in a somewhat different form, was brought into vogue by the work of the neurologist Möbius in 1900: *Die Anlage der Mathematik*. This theory is contradicted by anatomical facts and hardly squares with our knowledge that mathematical aptitude appears in widely different forms, and is generally associated with various other intellectual aptitudes.

Short of a more detailed analysis we shall merely list some factors which together go into the making of this mathematical aptitude. Interest in mathematical research itself; perspicacity in the choice of subjects; general methods; a more or less direct intuition of the results to be obtained, the obstacle to be surmounted and the particular means to be employed; and perseverance and method in the presentation of the definite solution, are the principal qualities of mind common to all creative mathematicians.

LOGICIANS AND INTUITIONISTS

We shall now give our attention to the essential differences that can exist between various creative minds, and here again Poincaré gives us the most fruitful starting point. In a famous chapter of his *La Valeur de la Science*[1] Poincaré distinguishes between two main categories of mathematicians:

'The first, above all, are preoccupied with logic. While reading their works we may be tempted to believe that they have only advanced step by step, like a Vauban who raised his trench-works against fortifications, leaving nothing to chance. The others let themselves be guided by intuition, and from the start advance, if sometimes precariously, like a dashing cavalry vanguard.

'It is not the subject matter itself that dictates the method they are to use. If the former are often called analysts, and the others geometricians, this does not alter the fact that the former remain analysts even when they are geometricians, while the others still remain geometricians even when they deal with pure analysis. It is the very nature of their minds which makes them either logicians or

---

[1] '*L'intuition et la logique en Mathématiques*' in *La Valeur de la Science*, Paris, Flammarion, 1913.

intuitionists and they cannot escape from this when they tackle a new subject.

'Nor is it education that brings out one of these two tendencies and stifles the other. Mathematicians are born, not bred, and it would also seem that one is born either a geometrician or an analyst.'[1]

Poincaré sees examples of logicians in Méray, Hermite, Weierstrass and Sophie Kowalevski; and of intuitionists in Klein, Joseph Bertrand, Riemann and Sophus Lie. With regard to this question, J. Hadamard[2] shows that in Poincaré's classification the distinction between intuitive and logical minds has, in fact, two very different aspects.

As regards the case of Hermite, Hadamard points out that even if this scientist did not employ a single concrete image in his thoughts, and even if he had some measure of revulsion against geometry in his discoveries and in the way he presented them, intuition had nevertheless played an important part, 'the methods apparently arising in his mind by some mysterious means'.

As a further example supporting his thesis, Hadamard also cites the flash of genius which was the starting point of Weierstrass in the construction of his new method of the calculus of variations.

Applying this very judicious remark to an interpretation of the mental work in a discovery due to the unconscious, Hadamard shows that according to one point of view the distinction between intuitive and logical minds arises from the fact that mental work takes place either in a more or in a less deep zone of the unconscious; he notes, furthermore, that a number of scientists are logicians in appearance only, i.e. in the enunciation of their ideas, after they have been intuitives in discovering them. According to Hadamard, some of the other factors distinguishing between the various types of mathematical minds are the degree of precision in one's approach, the degree of apparent mental order, auxiliary mental pictures supporting mental progress, and finally the extent to which the faculty of making fruitful use of theories or algorithms is developed.

[1] *Op. cit.*
[2] *The Psychology of Invention.*

THE ORIENTATION OF RESEARCH WORK

We shall finally pose the essential problem of the general trend of the mathematician's efforts. In a work that appeared quite some time ago, and that was devoted chiefly to the role of chance in discovery,[1] Paul Souriau, the psychologist, considers vanity as the main source of creative activity, a young scientist being mainly concerned with 'attracting public attention' or with 'establishing a pleasant and independent position for himself'. This would imply a profound lack of desire on the part of the scientist to participate in the difficult process of arriving at the truth. Ambition, vanity and the rewards of a career are certainly motivations whose role must not be underestimated. We have only to recall some famous quarrels, and to remember Charles Nicolle's remark, stated with his customary forthrightness, that 'without ambition and without vanity, no-one would enter a profession so contrary to our natural appetites'. However, these reasons alone would not have led to the splendid developments of science and, in fact, we must not neglect a much worthier one that has had a very much more fruitful influence, i.e. that love of science by which all great research workers are animated. Although this is not the sole cause, many discoveries of importance would never have been made without it, since far from satisfying the vanity of their authors or giving them any advantages, they forced them to engage in a painful and unequal struggle against prejudice, routine and vested interests. This is so much the case that many scientists prefer to leave some of their most revolutionary discoveries unpublished, fearing that unless they did so they would have to engage in exhausting polemics. We shall return to this general aspect of scientific discovery in some greater detail.

A point concerning mathematical creativity in particular is the problem of its usefulness. This question has been the object of many keen controversies, of which the most celebrated was that between Fourier and Jacobi in 1830. Author of the *Théorie analytique de la Chaleur*, Fourier had contributed most brilliantly both to the birth of mathematical physics and also to an essential advance in analysis: the introduction of trigonometric series. Because of his own tastes

[1] *Théorie de L'Invention*, Paris, 1881.

and the general trend of his work, he did not fully appreciate the importance of some mathematical studies which he considered to be purely theoretical. Such a point of view was legitimate, since each scientist has a marked predilection for a particular domain of research, but in reporting to the *Académie des Sciences* some of Abel and Jacobi's basic work on elliptic integrals, Fourier made the great mistake of trying to impose his personal taste on others, and of stating his regret that scientists of such worth should choose to spend their time on purely theoretical research, rather than on the solution of problems of mathematical physics. In a letter to Legendre, Jacobi replied to this remark with some indignation:

'It is true that M. Fourier believes that the chief aim of mathematics is its public usefulness and its explanation of natural phenomena, but a philosopher like him ought to have known that the sole aim of science is to do honour to the human spirit, and that in this respect a question about numbers is as important as a question about the system of the Universe.'[1]

The sudden death of Fourier put a stop to this polemic, but the fruitful influence of some of Fourier's results on pure mathematics, and equally the relevance of Jacobi's work to applied mathematics, show clearly that an originator can but rarely evaluate the subsequent repercussions of his own discoveries.

Furthermore, from purely utilitarian considerations, it cannot be denied that the theoretical discoveries which have had the richest results in the applied field have often been those which in their original form had appeared as the most abstract, and as furthest removed from all concrete consideration. Thus, theoretical research work is of primary interest to the progress of the applied sciences.

'Those who are most disdainful of theory,' says Poincaré very justly, 'unwittingly earn their daily bread from it; deprive them of it, and progress would soon come to an end.'[2]

Thus the lack of interest which most mathematicians display in the immediate applications of their discoveries is quite understandable. Furthermore we could easily compile an impressive list of theoretical facts that proves their subsequent fruitfulness in the

[1] Letter dated the 2nd July, 1830.
[2] *La Valeur de la Science.*

applied field. In this connection M. Hadamard tells the following very striking anecdote:

'Once, during my long and fruitful conversations with Pierre Duhem, I told him that I had arrived at a theorem on the composition of analytic functions, and gave him my formulation of it. I thought that I had best leave it to the future to worry about any possible applications it might have. Being both a physicist and an artist Duhem compared me with a painter who started by sketching a landscape in his room and then carried his canvas in search of a site which seemed to fit the picture. However, this embarrassing comparison did not disconcert me, and in the end it was I who was proved right. Applications began to follow and today there are very many of them. I was unreservedly proud of the elegance of my enunciation and this feeling did not deceive me.'[1]

Another typical example is that of the French mathematician Elie Cartan, who in 1913 discovered a remarkable class of analytical and geometrical transformations concerning the theory of groups. At that time no practical considerations could have led to a study of these transformations, and Cartan's research work was guided by nothing but a feeling for mathematical aesthetics, for which Poincaré had justly reserved an essential place. Some fifteen years later, however, this discovery showed its practical value in the demonstration of some electrical phenomena, which could not have been interpreted except by means of the transformations studied by Cartan in 1913.[2]

Thus history tells us of very many theoretical discoveries which afterwards proved fruitful in the applied field.

Conversely, many theoretical advances owe their origin to practical sources. Physics has frequently been a great help to mathematics, by suggesting the kind of problem that theoreticians would never have dreamt of, and by suggesting, out of a tremendous number of unresolved questions, those that were to prove of exceptional fruitfulness.

To return to the example of Cartan; if from the work of this great mathematician we can choose many other examples similar to that quoted above, where theoretical discoveries have had im-

---

[1] *IXᵉ Semaine Intern. de Synth.*
[2] J. Hadamard, *The Psychology of Invention.*

portant subsequent repercussions in the field of mathematical physics, it is undeniable that some of his work was inspired to a greater or lesser degree by his wish to contribute to the development of new physical theories.

Thus there are really two points of view, two complementary attitudes, which only *appear* to contradict each other. True, in their research work, most mathematicians allow themselves to be guided by nothing but purely theoretical considerations, while others, on the contrary, dedicate their efforts exclusively to problems that can be applied immediately. Yet there are some who, like Newton, Gauss, Hamilton, Poincaré and Cartan, have a great breadth of vision, great powers of conception and considerable virtuosity, so that they can profit from the two most fruitful sources of inspiration: feelings for mathematical harmony and for physical reality.

Once again Poincaré gives us the most convincing justification of this point of view. Insisting that mathematics has a triple aim, i.e. physical, mathematical and aesthetic, he claims that the physical and aesthetic aims 'are inseparable, and (that) the best means of obtaining the one is to look at the other or at least never to lose sight of it'. In support of this opinion he recalls first of all that mathematics supply the physicist with 'the only language that he can speak' and that it teaches him 'to recognize true and profound similarities unseen by the eyes but devised by the mind'. In this connection he quotes three famous examples, Newton's law of universal gravitation, and Maxwell's and Laplace's equations. However, physics, in its turn, suggests to the mathematician not only a number of most important problems, but, beyond this, it often guides him to the best methods of arriving at a solution. In this connection the introduction of continuous magnitudes and of trigonometric series, the elaboration of the notion of functions, the development of the theory of partial differential equations are particularly convincing examples.[1]

We may, apparently, draw some conclusions from this brief analysis. The best guide in choosing a particular approach in research, i.e. the essential operations determining the importance and scope of a particular work, is the aesthetic sense that is to some extent inherent in all mathematicians. Whether this sentiment is completely inspired

---

[1] 'L'Analyse et la physique' in *La Valeur de la Science*.

C

by feelings of theoretical harmony, or whether it is more or less directly influenced by a sense of physical reality, is basically nothing but a question of the temperament and the personal taste of a particular mathematician. Furthermore, this diversity of talent is very fortunate indeed, for the harmonious progress of science only results from the combined efforts of many different minds. Conversely, a keen desire for immediate and exact applications often leads to nothing but problems of very limited scope, contributing only incidentally to the development of science.

CHAPTER II

THEORETICAL SCIENCES

In the vast realm of theoretical science, ranging as it does from the frontiers of mathematics to those of the experimental and observational sciences, the conditions of discovery are, in many respects, close to those of mathematical inventions. Nevertheless, they differ very considerably in some essential points, since, in order to establish his hypotheses or theories, the theoretician must be supported by observation or experiment.

THE BEGINNING OF A NEW SUBJECT FOR RESEARCH

Thus, theoretical creation appears to be some kind of intermediary between invention and discovery. It starts from an initial idea which generally arises out of a state of affairs that previous theories had been unable to explain. M. Louis de Broglie has painted a very vivid picture of this initial phase in the work of creation:

'Whenever we begin studying a subject, we are necessarily confronted by the particular "state of the question". Some facts are well known, some facts well established, some ideas generally held. Finally, some difficulties are frankly recognized or very often easily glossed over. Now it sometimes happens that, in studying a certain scientific field, the inventive theoretician feels a sort of uneasiness which becomes more and more acute. Slowly but steadily he begins to feel that an essential element is lacking in our interpretation, and that the fundamental idea has been misunderstood, thus making impossible a true understanding of the facts. No longer does he dismiss the gaps in previous theories as mere anomalies that will disappear when they are correctly fitted into the field as a whole, but rather as a shortcoming of the theories themselves. His keen interest aroused, he becomes aware of a mass of small and apparently unconnected facts, and he begins to suspect hidden relationships that can only be explained by a theory based on entirely new ideas. Thus a geologist, surveying a vast region formed by recent alluvial deposits, and noticing the emergence of occasional outcrops of granite, may suddenly suspect that here has emerged a deep layer of ancient formations, once the shelf of the entire region, and explaining its structure. Thus small facts that were apparently pure accidents or anomalies suddenly appear as external signs of a previously un-recognized but fundamental unity.'[1]

FLASHES OF THOUGHT

After the period of preparation, in which the creator has learnt to appreciate the difficulties in his path, the analogies to be explained, and the real or apparent connections that he must elucidate, directive ideas are slowly formed and organized more or less consciously in his mind.

'Then, quite suddenly and generally with a jolt there occurs some kind of crystallization, and the research worker perceives instantly and very clearly, and from then on perfectly consciously, the main outlines of the new concepts that were latent in him, and at a stroke he arrives at the absolute certainty that the implementation of these new concepts will allow him to solve most of the problems posed, and to elucidate the entire question by revealing clearly those similarities and harmonies that were previously unknown.'[2]

As is the case in mathematics, this flash of thought, this *Geistes-blitz*, does not generally appear during periods of assiduous work, but rather during those of rest or relaxation, since the nervous tension produced by periods of active research opposes the 'spon-taneous reorganization of ideas, the kind of psychological com-pression from which light suddenly flashes out'. Thus maturing slowly as a result of previous effort and of the work of the sub-conscious, a discovery will suddenly appear at such times as the investigator's mind did not seem to be dealing with it.[3]

In this phase of the work of discovery, aesthetic feelings intervene most fruitfully and permit the scientist to foresee the importance and scope of his discovery. Some authors have interpreted these feelings

[1] '*L'Invention Scientifique. Les Sciences Experimentales. Théorie*', in IXe *Semaine Intern. de Synthèse.*

[2] *Ibid.*

[3] In this connection we must also quote P. Langevin's reply to P. Valéry, during a meeting of the *Société française de Philosophie:* 'The moments in which you claim to feel that something within you is becoming released, occur constantly in my personal experience.' (Quoted by J. Hadamard, *Subconscient, intuition et logique dans la recherche scientifique.* Lecture at the *Palais de la Découverte*, 8th December, 1945.)

as manifestations of some sort of 'economy of thought', but the growing complexity of physical theories would clearly seem to contradict them. In fact, as in mathematics, the beauty of a theory is less the result of its simplicity than of its explanatory value, and of the syntheses of previously unconnected facts that it helps to make.

OBTAINING RESULTS

When a flash of thought has shown him a new path, the task of the research worker is far from finished. He must now harness the arguments which will establish the validity of his ideas, and deduce all their implications, check predictions based upon them with experimental results, answer all possible objections, and finally set limits to the theory. This stage of the work is by no means without difficulties since, as the theory becomes more clearly defined, there will arise innumerable complications in the details, which must be overcome slowly and painstakingly. Above all, after the moment of enthusiasm following upon the sudden revelation of a new theory, the creative physicist will begin to note its limited and provisional character with ever greater clarity. Even if most observed facts can be satisfactorily explained in the initial phase of the research work, others will slowly appear, the interpretation of which may prove more difficult if not impossible. This realization is apt to check the initial enthusiasm rather quickly. Yet another factor intervenes more and more acutely, i.e. the more complex the theories the more difficult it is to understand them clearly. Returning to his theories and attempting to build them on solid foundations, and to explain them as clearly as possible, the theoretician may notice that their deep significance remains shrouded in some obscurity, and this often tempers his joy with 'a slight sentiment of bitterness—the final realization of the fragmentary and limited character of the advances he has made'.[1]

THE PROVISIONAL CHARACTER OF THEORIES

This provisional and limited character of each new hypothesis is much more apparent in the domain of theoretical physics than it is in mathematics, where advances are most frequently made by successive contributions not involving the preliminary destruction of

[1] L. de Broglie in *L'Invention*.

parts of the previous structure. In this respect the difficulties that were encountered in the interpretation of the principal theories of physics are very suggestive. If electronic theory, quantum theory and wave mechanics have permitted the explanation of many phenomena and the prediction of new ones, nevertheless the basic ideas cannot be explained convincingly enough, and there remains a slight feeling of uneasiness which sometimes becomes very marked.

THE CONSOLIDATION OF THEORIES

This ill-ease which very often arises in penetrating minds which study problems without any preconceived ideas, and without adhering too literally to the prevailing ideas on the subject, is due partly to the impression that some of the difficulties are more or less consciously disguised. In the course of his discovery, the creative theoretician will certainly have become aware, at least partially so, of the limits, the gaps, and the obscurities in the new theory that he has created, and he will often recognize its fragmentary and pro-visional character. But it so happens that, to justify and explain it the better, he is led into insisting on the success rather than on the gaps. Furthermore, it happens frequently that:

'Rash disciples, or those blinded by uncritical enthusiasm, may transform into rigid dogma what, to the master's more critical mind, appears as one of the incomplete and provisional links in the infinite chain of attempts and successive approximations produced by scientific thought in the course of its forward march.'[1]

This progressive transformation into dogmas of theories which, while they may be essential phases in scientific progress, are nothing but provisional stages, occurs frequently and is an important illustra-tion of man's tendency to adopt less and less critically and more and more dogmatically a theory or hypothesis whose limitations and imperfections he keenly resents. Later on we shall come across other theories which, after playing a most fruitful part, subsequently obstructed the progress of science for many long years. For the

[1] L. de Broglie in *L'Invention*. Cf. also the evidence of Paul Langevin in the same collection: 'In these successive advances which we try to make, the successors have a much more rigid point of view than had the creators of the doctrine. It is certain that the exponents of the law of action at a distance believed in it far more firmly than Newton did himself. Clearly Newton and Galileo would not have opposed relativity quite so desperately.'

moment we shall merely quote some particularly suggestive examples of this two-fold action, first progressive and then retro-
gressive: in chemistry we had Stahl's phlogiston theory in the
eighteenth century, and in the nineteenth century the theory of
equivalents; in physics, there was the caloric theory which, after
having been most useful, was an obstacle to the subsequent development of thermodynamics, the famous theory of energetics which
played a very unfortunate part at the end of the nineteenth century,
the ether hypothesis, and finally the belief in the general continuity
of natural processes and in the absolute nature of time and space.
Writing history is almost like the reconstruction of the entire
evolution of physical theory; every new theory appears to be
constructed somehow as a reaction against the faults and imperfections of a previous one.

CHAPTER III

OBSERVATIONAL AND EXPERIMENTAL SCIENCES

THE CHOICE OF A SUBJECT

In the domain of the experimental sciences a discovery often arises from a feeling of dissatisfaction with the obscurity of a point. The research worker is confronted with a fact or a series of facts which apparently do not agree with previous theories or explanatory hypotheses. This fact or this series of facts may emerge from systematic observations, from accidental findings, or again from a thorough critical examination of previous results. Once the existence of an apparently erroneous fact is assumed to be solidly established, the research worker is confronted by what is frequently a very complex question, whose solution will often lead him to a discovery: how can he square this fact with all the known data, in a manner that is both most rational and most satisfying to the mind?

A second path also may lead to a discovery in the experimental domain. Whenever a new theory appears, or when old theories seem to be inadequately supported, the experimenter is logically forced to confront reality with the consequences of the theory, and this comparison may throw up the initial idea of the discovery.

PREPARATORY WORK

This confrontation presupposes the discovery of new experimental data, and the consolidation of a plan of work allowing the implementation of a crucial experiment to test the value of the particular theory. In the choice both of apparatus and of the most fruitful method, the research worker is guided not only by a profound understanding of all the aspects of the phenomena under review and of all the results previously obtained, but very particularly by a special instinct of physical reality that helps him to obviate errors or false moves. Nevertheless, as in mathematics, or in the domain of theoretical science, much research work and much reflection must often precede the crystallization of a fruitful idea on which success depends. Thus, according to E. Bauer, the research worker follows 'an experimental path, in the way that a gun dog follows the game to the kill'. The German physicist Hertz gave a particularly telling description of this long effort in a letter to his parents in which he told them of his cathode ray experiments:

'For the moment, I am blundering without precise method. I repeat old experiments in this field and demonstrate others which pass through my head. . . . I hope that, among the hundred remarkable phenomena which I come across, some light will shine from one or another.'[1]

Again, in a conversation reported by J. Hadamard,[2] F. Joliot mentions the importance of these flashes of thought:

'Indeed I have had sudden flashes showing me the best way of producing or of observing phenomena, coupled with an immediate sensation that the method thus suggested is unique and that all others would be less simple.

'This sensation is rare, and I for one can only recall two occasions on which it occurred.'

Hadamard mentions the importance of one of these discoveries appearing in this abrupt way: the proof of the fission of the uranium atom.

THE EXPLOITATION OF GAINS

But when, owing to sudden intuitions generally coming after long methodical efforts, the problem to be solved is clearly fixed, and when the research worker has tried to design a precise method that would lead to success, he still needs a great deal of patience before he can hope to attain the desired goal. To do so he must concentrate on the different aspects of the problem to be solved, and he must often design very complicated experimental arrangements in which he needs to follow a rigorous method, and also to display great ingenuity in each separate experiment. To appreciate the patience that the research worker wishing to attain a desired end must display, we need only recall the painful, laborious and long but systematic research work of the Dutch physicist Kamerlingh Onnes and his collaborators at the Cryogenic Laboratory of Leyden in

[1] As quoted by E. Bauer, 'L'Invention Scientifique, II, Experimentation'. (IXe, Semaine Int. de Synth.).

[2] Subconscient, intuition et logique dans la recherche scientifique.

their attempts to liquefy helium and in arriving at the major discovery of supraconductivity. We may equally well quote the painful and laborious work of fractionation which led Pierre and Marie Curie to the discovery of radium.

While the theoretician has only to tackle the complexity of the phenomena to be interpreted, and the theoretical calculations to be made, the experimenter's work meets additional difficulties of a material order. In order to overcome these, he must have the combined qualities of a draughtsman, an engineer or even a precision worker, and, furthermore, some very special abilities involved in the handling of delicate apparatus and in carrying out his measurements to the limit of instrumental possibilities. The apparatus that he constructs must be thought out and calculated to the smallest detail, and he must bear in mind the very complicated factors that often intervene. Despite all precautions, disagreeable surprises frequently force him to modify, or even to change completely, the apparatus that he has so patiently constructed. Thus it often happens that the results differ profoundly from what he had expected. When confronted by unforeseen circumstances he must have a very keen gift of intuition and observation, so that he may rapidly discern the fundamental causes of any discrepancies in the theory, and then decide whether it is due to any unsuspected experimental difficulties, or to a new fact that may well lead to an unforeseen discovery. It is when speaking of this type of discovery that arises from the observation of unexpected phenomena that we generally insist on the part played by chance in the work of discovery. We shall return to this point in greater detail, but here we shall merely stress the fact that this so-called chance is never fruitful unless the experimenter is sufficiently ready to exploit it.

LIMITATIONS IMPOSED BY APPARATUS

We must make a final comment on the subject of this long and indispensable work of experimentation in arriving at a discovery. Its success is conditioned not only by the intelligence and the experimental qualities of the research worker, but also by the technical possibilities at his disposal. Many experiments, carried out methodically, have not led their originators to the discoveries that they had hoped for, because the instruments and means of observation or measurement were too rudimentary to produce the expected result. Here we have an instance of premature research work which will not come to fruition until such time as the improvement of technical means will allow it to be tackled more effectively. Owing to this fact, the level reached by experimental science at a particular epoch depends both on the state of technique and on the improvements in the theory. It is for this reason that the study of electrical discharges in rarefied gases was largely influenced by the facilities of the apparatus designed for creating a vacuum. Instruments, we must repeat, play an essential part in experimental discovery and each improvement may lead to corresponding new discoveries. The invention and improvements of the astronomical telescope have led to all those advances made in observational astronomy since the seventeenth century, which, together with the development of mathematical analysis, have been the cause of the subsequent progress in celestial mechanics.

THE BIOLOGICAL SCIENCES

So far we have emphasized the physical sciences. In the domain of the biological sciences the problem of discovery arises in a similar way, although here observation plays an even more essential part, and the interpretation of facts is rendered more delicate by the greater complexity of the elements involved. The famous pages devoted by Claude Bernard, in his *Introduction à l'étude de la médicine expérimentale* to discoveries in the medical field, and in that of the observational and experimental sciences, have so profound a significance that all new detailed studies can be nothing but commentaries on it. The various stages in the making of a discovery described by this famous biologist are just those that have been put forward in previous chapters.

'A true scientist is one who combines in himself both theory and experimental practice.

1. He discovers a fact.
2. An idea, connected with this fact, is born in his mind.
3. On the basis of this idea he reasons, makes an experiment, and conceives and implements the necessary material conditions.
4. From this experiment, new phenomena appear which he must then observe, and so forth.'

THE OBJECTIVITY OF THE RESEARCH WORKER

An essential point, insisted upon by Claude Bernard, and the great importance of which we have already noted, is the necessity of systematic doubt, of complete mental freedom when confronted by generally held theories. In the domain of the physical or biological sciences all discoveries do, in fact, produce a partial recasting of accepted theories and hypotheses, and require great independence of mind and undeniable intellectual courage on the part of their authors. Nevertheless, this doubt must not preclude the experimenter from holding any *a priori* ideas; it must only persuade him that no idea is valuable unless an experiment can establish its validity or verify its consequences. An experiment without any *a priori* assumptions whatever runs the grave risk of being sterile. It only becomes of interest when it is made with the intention of assessing the validity of, or dismissing, the hypothesis which initiated it.

'People who have excessive faith in their theories or in their ideas,' Claude Bernard says, 'are not only badly placed for making discoveries, they also make very bad observations; (we must) never make experiments in order to confirm our ideas, but simply in order to control them.'

This sensible remark is coupled with equally fruitful advice, namely not to make experiments with the sole aim of 'finding fault with the theories of others or of trying to contradict them'.

This advice must, however, not be taken too literally; the experimenter must not be afraid of finding a theory wrong or even of demolishing it, but he must not make too deliberate an effort in this direction, since this might be detrimental to a sound analysis of the results, and even to objective observations or measurements.

Since the time when Claude Bernard wrote his admirable essay, there have been quite a few developments in biology and the natural sciences. Slowly, as observational and measuring instruments were perfected and the field of knowledge became broader, research conditions in this vast sector began to approach those in the physical sciences. However, the resemblance is still not close enough for prudence and reflection to be dispensed with since, very often, the phenomena can only be observed qualitatively.

PART TWO

Factors in Discovery

CHAPTER IV

SYSTEMATIC DISCOVERY

THE study of the various realms of discovery has enabled us to give evidence of the main laws governing the genesis of a discovery. We have seen, in particular, that a rigorous and rational scientific method will remain the research worker's best guide. If certain circumstances, to which we shall refer later, can influence the trend of work favourably or unfavourably, there can yet be no doubt that rigour and method are indispensable during any phase of research work. Nevertheless, we must not forget that the personal qualities of the scientist have an essential part to play, and that even by applying the laws of scientific method most rigorously, the research worker, if he is not sufficiently talented, will not make anything but secondary discoveries. Fruitful intuition, a great mind for synthesis, and an informed sense of reality, are the essential qualities characterizing the creative scientist.

INTUITION AND LOGIC

In fact, each scientist has an original personality which depends largely on the emphasis he places on intuition. While the intuitive relies mainly on his 'illuminations', his flashes of genius, to show him the most fruitful path, the logician prefers to follow a more rigorous method and a more austere and systematic road.

It is probably in mathematics that we meet the greatest proportion of 'logical' minds, whose discoveries are essentially the result of thorough analyses, the systematic exploitation of previous work, or the methodical study of problems. We need only think of Euler and Lagrange, and to recall the cases quoted by Poincaré.

Also suggestive are the examples of Coulomb, Maxwell and Fresnel in theoretical science, and of Claude Bernard and Pasteur in the experimental sciences.

But a closer examination of the work of all these scientists will show that method alone cannot explain the fruitfulness of their work. It is no more than an instrument which, to be used in the best

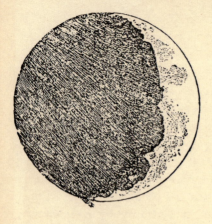

Fig. 1.—*The Moon before first quarter.* 'Already four or five days after conjunction, when bright patches can be distinguished on the Moon, the demarcation line between bright and dark regions does not follow a uniform oval path, as would be the case with a perfectly spherical object. The dividing line is unequal, coarse and winding, as illustrated by the figure. In fact, many bright protuberances extend from the bright into the dark region, while small dark areas encroach upon the illuminated zone' (Galileo, *Sidereus Nuncius*).

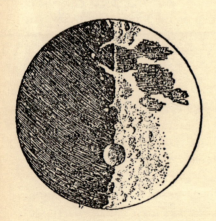

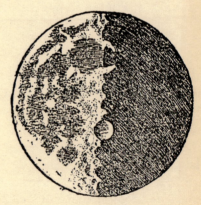

Fig. 2 and Fig. 3.—*The Moon at first quarter* (left) *and at last quarter* (right). '. . . Both at first and second quarter, large protuberances can be seen above and below a certain spot occupying the upper or northern expanse of the Moon, as shown in the figures' (Galileo, *Sidereus Nuncius*).

Note the rough character of the drawings which, however, show the lunar accurately enough. The craters, on the contrary, are badly situated. These drawings are orientated in the reverse way to modern representations.

PLATE I

Et Mellan Gal. pinx. et sculp

Phœnix Aquis sextus. An. 1635 Octob. 7 a claro adhuc crepusculo in occasu vso

MAP OF THE MOON AT FIRST QUARTER, DRAWN AND ENGRAVED BY CLAUDE MELLAN,
UNDER THE DIRECTION OF THE ASTRONOMERS PEIRESC AND GASSENDI

(*The observation was dated 7th October, 1635*)

*If one compares this etching with Galileo's drawing (Fig. 2), it will be seen that
Mellan's is the more meticulous, detailed and accurate of the two. Mellan's was, in fact,
the first real map of the Moon.*

PLATE II

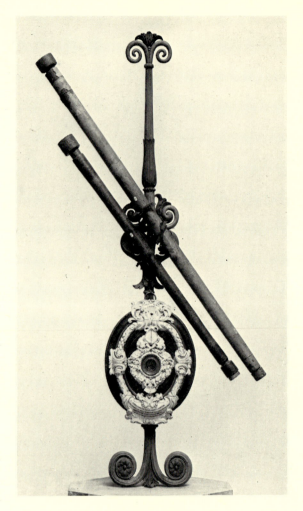

TWO OF THE ASTRONOMICAL TELESCOPES CONSTRUCTED BY
GALILEO, NOW IN THE HISTORY OF SCIENCE MUSEUM
AT FLORENCE

These very primitive instruments consist of a simple (richly ornamented) cardboard tube holding the objective (a converging lens) and the eyepiece (a diverging lens). Because of the poor quality of the glass, and also because of the crude methods of grinding and polishing, the instruments were unsatisfactory and gave only small magnifications. The supports themselves show how primitive were the methods of observation. It was only in the second half of the seventeenth century that astronomical telescopes and instruments for making angular measurements, mounted on stable supports, came into use. This improved apparatus led to great advances in positional astronomy.

PLATE III

INTERIOR VIEW OF THE DOME OF THE PALOMAR MOUNTAIN OBSERVATORY (U.S.A.),
SHOWING THE MOST IMPORTANT PARTS OF THE WORLD'S LARGEST TELESCOPE. THE
DIAMETER OF THE MIRROR IS 200 INCHES. GALAXIES UP TO A DISTANCE OF 2,000
MILLION LIGHT-YEARS HAVE BEEN OBSERVED WITH THIS TELESCOPE

*A comparison of this instrument with Galileo's primitive apparatus (see Plate II) is
symbolic of the great advance astronomy has made during the last three centuries.*

PLATE IV

manner, should only be applied to carefully chosen problems. If, in the case of these 'logical' minds, intuition would seem to play a less obvious part than in that of the so-called 'intuitives', its influence nevertheless remains essential: it is only that the work of discovery is here more clearly directed and that it is more rigorous and more methodical than that of the intuitive scientists.

GUIDING THOUGHTS

There are various elements that may guide the scientific worker. Sometimes a precise problem presents itself to the scientist, as, for instance, in the case of Pasteur's main discoveries.

In many other cases research is guided by general ideas which are often very fruitful: the idea of invariance which appears in different forms in both mathematics and physics; the idea of analogy on which the most elegant syntheses are based; the wish to generalize a theory that appears too fragmentary; the urge to explain experimental facts or empirical formulae; or finally the idea of verifying experimental theories or hypotheses that are insufficiently established.

But even in the case of the most methodical minds, these general ideas have superimposed on them more particular ideas, on which

PLATE IV

PART OF THE MOON'S SURFACE AS SEEN
THROUGH A MODERN TELESCOPE

A comparison with Figs. 1, 2 and 3, and with Plate I, will serve to emphasize the extent of modern advances in this field. The photograph shows the Mare Tranquillitatis and the Mare Serenitatis, separated by the Haemus Mountains, in the N.E. region of the Moon. A number of well-known craters can be distinguished: Arago in the Mare Tranquillitatis; Pliny and Jansen S.E. of the Haemus Mountains; Menelaus to the East, and Posidonius to the N.E. An important crevice runs S.W. of Arago.

D

depends the success or the importance of the research work. It is the value and the fertility of these particular and personal ideas that characterize the true genius.

Abel's idea of replacing the study of the elliptic integral by that of the inverse function extended to the complex domain, Torricelli's idea of replacing water by mercury to help him improve his investigations of the barometer, Fresnel's idea in explaining the phenomena of polarization by the transverse nature of the vibrations of light, Max von Laue's idea of using a crystal as a grating for demonstrating the diffraction of X-rays, are only some examples, amongst many, of manifestations of genius, without which even the most rigorous method would run the risk of becoming quite pointless.

Nevertheless, this is by no means an absolute law, and we could cite many discoveries in whose genesis scientific method proved its intrinsic fruitfulness even in the absence of any particular sort of intuition. There could be no development of science if, side by side with these great minds whose brilliant ideas lead to new theories, new methods and new syntheses, there were not the often less brilliant research workers who, by their patient labours, exploit the possibilities within their reach and draw the necessary consequences.

THE DISCOVERY OF NEW PLANETS

The discovery of the planets Uranus, Neptune and Pluto are particularly significant examples of successes due both to rigorous and systematic observations and also to methodical and painstaking calculations.

Of the five planets visible to the naked eye, Mercury, Venus, Mars, Jupiter and Saturn have been known since antiquity. The invention of the telescope at the beginning of the seventeeth century introduced some new bodies adding to our picture of the solar system, viz. the first four satellites of Jupiter discovered by Galileo in January 1610; Titan, the largest satellite of Saturn, discovered by Huygens in March 1655; and the ring of Saturn, which, imperfectly observed by Galileo in 1610, was not explained correctly until Huygens did so in 1656.[1] But in the ensuing years, despite constant progress in methods of observation and the increased power and

[1] See p. 156 ff.

continual improvements of the telescope, no new discovery was to extend the list of planets in the solar system. It was only in 1781 when, in order to get a better understanding of the structure of the universe, the great English astronomer William Herschel (1783–1822) observed the different regions of the sky systematically with a powerful telescope of his own construction, that he noticed a new body near the constellation of Gemini, which he at first believed to be a comet. As Herschel was soon to realize on the basis of calculations by Laplace, Bochart de Saron, Lexell and Lalande, this was in fact a new planet whose orbit was beyond that of Saturn. Such was the first important discovery of a very talented observer who, within a few decades, was to rejuvenate many branches of astronomy. But it was difficult to predict with any accuracy the path of the new planet, whose current name Uranus soon replaced that of Georgium Sidus, proposed by Herschel in honour of his patron, King George III. The first tables calculated soon after Herschel's discovery were obviously inaccurate, since they were only based on observations of a very small fraction or the orbit of Uranus. (The duration of the revolution of that planet is in fact 84 years.) But with longer observation and as older accounts of the planet were checked in the Star Catalogues of Flamsteed (1690), of Mayer (1756), of Le Monnier (starting from 1734), etc., in which the planet was thought of as a fixed star, it seemed possible to construct tables allowing very accurate predictions of future displacements of Uranus. However, even with these highly satisfactory data, prediction did not agree with reality, nor show the expected degree of precision. Many astronomers tried to remedy this apparent disorder by means of improving the methods of calculation. It was thus that Alexis Bouvard (1767–1843), when adding an appendix containing tables of Uranus to the new edition of his *Nouvelles Tables des planets Jupiter et Saturne* in 1821, tried to correct the error by taking into account all the known observations and the perturbing actions of all the other planets. Nevertheless this astronomer, who was justly respected for the accuracy and rigour of his calculations, had to confess that his tables agreed only imperfectly with reality. In order to explain the discrepancy he made the hypothesis that a still unknown planet could perturb the motion of Uranus. This explanation was not received favourably at the time. Some astronomers, for instance Clairaut in his very provisional study of the theory of the Moon, thought that modifications of Newton's law or even attraction between the known planets could explain these anomalies. The great German astronomer Bessel (1784–1846), who had first of all supported one of these fantastic hypotheses, when writing to Alexander Humboldt some years later, had come round to Bouvard's opinion:

'I think the day will come when the mystery of Uranus will perhaps be solved by a new planet whose elements will be recognized by its action on Uranus and verified by that which it exerts on Saturn.'

Thus the problem of the perturber of Uranus was clearly posed. Some astronomers took up the research of this new planet, starting with its established effects on the motion of Uranus, but, daunted by the complexity of the calculations, they gave up before arriving at any useful results.

In 1841, however, a student of St. John's College, Cambridge, John Couch Adams (1819–1892), then twenty-two years old, found a solution to this problem, of which he gave a still imperfect account in a thesis which he submitted in 1843. From his research work Adams had obtained a series of much more accurate observations on the motion of Uranus, and in October 1845 he communicated to the Director of Greenwich Observatory a much closer estimate of the mass, the position and the various parts of the trajectory of the assumed perturbing planet. However, the official astronomers only attached small importance to this work, and their investigations to verify Adams' conjectures were too inadequate to lead to any positive conclusion. Further observations by Adams, giving new and more accurate results, did not fare any better, owing perhaps to the absence of a very accurate map of the region of the sky in which the new planet was assumed to be located. Not discouraged, Adams began to improve his calculations still further, so that he could make what he justly considered to be an inevitable and even imminent discovery. However, on the 30th September, 1846, he was to learn that the discovery had eluded him, at least in its decisive stage. A young French astronomer, Urbain le Verrier, had, in fact, also, and quite independently of Adams, predicted the existence of this new trans-Uranian planet, and the research work based on his indications undertaken by the German astronomer, Johann G. Galle, led to the discovery of this planet on the night of the 23rd to 24th September.

A former pupil of the *Ecole Polytechnique*, and former engineer of the State Tobacco Department, Le Verrier had been a research worker in chemistry and mathematics, when his nomination as lecturer in astronomy at the *Ecole Polytechnique* in 1837 decided his scientific career and guided him to the study of celestial mechanics. He started by tackling the difficult problems of perturbations and secular variations of the planetary orbits, and later the motion of Venus and the periodic return of the comets. In the papers which he published on these different subjects he showed great mental discipline and a rare mastery of difficult astronomical calculations. These qualities attracted the attention of Arago, the very active permanent secretary of the *Académie, des Sciences*, who, in 1845, advised him to study the causes of the established anomalies in the motion of Uranus. Le Verrier's first task was to set out the elements of the problem more accurately, to correct carefully the data of the old tables, and thus to determine the perturbation caused by Jupiter and Saturn. After these preliminary calculations, of which he published the results on the 10th November, 1845, the young astronomer, quite ignorant of the still unpublished work of Adams, proposed a new hypothesis that was able to explain this fact, namely that a still unknown trans-Uranian planet was the cause of these perturbations.

In giving an account of the results of this new stage of his work in a second paper dated 1st June, 1846, Le Verrier calculated, on the basis of Bode's empirical law, that the radius of the orbit of the new planet was approximately double that of Uranus, assuming that the plane of the desired orbit was nearly coincident with that of the ecliptic. These hypotheses, together with the established perturbations in the motion of Uranus, enabled him to evaluate the mass of the planet under consideration, the eccentricity and orientation of its orbital axis, and finally its position at any given time. These calculations were obviously very involved and delicate, since their purpose was to determine all the above factors on the basis of very inaccurate data, namely an effect on the motion of Uranus of which the order of magnitude was never greater than that of the errors of observation. Nevertheless Le Verrier, in his first calculations, managed to predict that on the 1st January 1847 the longitude of the planet would be 325° with a possible error of 10°.[1] Promising more exact results, he concluded:

'This work must be considered as the sketch of a theory which is only just beginning. I shall busy myself with improving it as much as possible.'

In fact, four months later, Le Verrier presented a new paper, *On the planet producing the observed anomalies in the motion of Uranus: determination of its mass, of its orbit and of its actual position*, in which he gave an accurate position of the planet, and a first approximation of its mass and apparent diameter. He pointed out that the planet happened then to be nearly at opposition with the sun and thus in a very favourable position for observation. Finally he gave various other details that could be used by other observers. However, since at the time the Observatory of Paris had neither an equatorial telescope of sufficient power to make the kind of investigation with confidence, nor a sufficiently accurate map of the particular region of the sky, on the 18th September, 1846, Le Verrier wrote to Johann G. Galle, then the assistant to J. F. Encke at the Berlin Observatory, communicating his conclusions and asking Galle to carry out a search for the trans-Uranian planet, of which he had predicted the existence. Galle received this letter on the 23rd September and, despite the scepticism of his Director, he began the investigation on the same evening, assisted by a young student, H. L. d'Arrest. Using a new and still unfinished map of the sky which was the work of Bremiker, Galle, on that very evening, discovered the desired planet only 52′ away from the position that Le Verrier had suggested. A further observation on the next day showed that this body had been displaced by one degree, and that it was therefore a planet. Galle wrote immediately to Le Verrier communicating his successful discovery: 'The planet of which you have given the position, really exists.'[2]

After having announced this triumph to the *Académie des Sciences* on the 5th October, 1846, Le Verrier concluded with somewhat

[1] This result, which was, in fact, more accurate than the margin of error would lead one to suppose, only differed by 1° from the estimate submitted by Adams to the Greenwich Observatory seven months earlier.

[2] This discovery of Neptune is one of the most characteristic examples of the convergence of discoveries; we shall mention further cases on page 131.

ambitious words of hope, of which the partial truth was established by the discovery of the trans-Neptunian planet Pluto on the 12th March, 1930, by C. W. Tombaugh at the Lowell Observatory, Flagstaff, Arizona:

'This success encourages us to hope that, after thirty or forty years of observation of the new planet, we should be able to use it in its turn for discovering the planet next in order of distance from the sun. Continuing this process, we should eventually arrive at planets which, because of their immense distance from the sun, would be invisible, but whose orbits may be mapped with great accuracy in the course of centuries, by means of the theory of secular inequalities.'

In actual fact, when the astronomers Percival Lowell (1855–1916) and E. C. Pickering (1846–1919), by making some modifications to the work of Adams and Le Verrier, could forecast the position of Pluto with some accuracy, their calculations were chiefly based on the residual perturbations of the motion of Uranus. Those of Neptune were still too difficult to be evaluated accurately, since from the time of its discovery the planet has traversed no more than two-thirds of its orbit. Furthermore, as we use perturbations of decreasing significance, the accuracy of our calculation must necessarily become smaller. It must finally be noted that because of its weak luminosity (it has magnitude 15) Pluto could never have been observed except through very powerful instruments. It was first discovered by means of an entirely modern method, i.e. the blink microscope, an instrument with which one can compare two photographs of the same sector of the sky, taken at different times.

Thus the circumstances of the discovery of the three new planets, of which we have just spoken and which have slowly led to an extension of the dimensions of the Solar system, have clear resemblances, and also very appreciable differences. Their most common characteristic is the fact that all three illustrate in a different form the effectiveness of patient and painstaking methodical research; i.e. the systematic observation of various regions of the sky in the case of Herschel's discovery of Uranus, the rational and attentive use made of the laws of celestial mechanics and of the method of residuals in the case of Adams and Le Verrier's discovery of Neptune, accurate and methodical calculations and the systematic scrutiny of previous observations in the case of the discovery of Pluto.

True, we may think that Herschel was very fortunate since, at the outset, he was unaware of having discovered a new planet. It is also true that Adams and Le Verrier were favoured by fortunate factors, which compensated for the considerable errors made by them both in evaluating the mean distance between Uranus and the Sun, and the eccentricity of the orbit of that planet. But this does not alter the fact that these three discoveries remain outstanding examples of the potentialities of the scientific method when applied in a rational and rigorous fashion either to simple observation or to calculations resulting from the systematic use of the general principles of celestial mechanics.

CHAPTER V

THE FRUITFULNESS OF SOME DISCOVERIES

IN the history of science there are many examples of discoveries or inventions whose emergence into the scientific world gave rise to a host of new work of different nature and importance.

This mechanism can operate in two very different ways. When a new method has been conceived or when a new instrument has been put at the disposal of observers or experimenters, research workers are, in general, attracted by the new paths that have been opened into previously unexploited realms, and new details and many results are quickly gathered. The second way is that of chain discoveries which, by means of more or less logical connections, all derive from an initial discovery.

ASSOCIATED DISCOVERIES

When a scientist of genius has discovered an original method opening up new paths for research, many scientists, tempted by hopes of relatively easy discoveries, immediately try to use this new tool for the most different purposes.

From their several efforts there soon emerge many new results of varied importance which, while gushing out in no small disorder, nevertheless provide the elements for new syntheses.

The Infinitesimal Calculus

A particularly typical example in mathematics is that of the many problems of very different origin treated by Leibniz and his followers at the end of the seventeenth and the beginning of the eighteenth centuries. The discovery of the notation of the infinitesimal calculus opened up to the mathematicians new methods of extreme fruitfulness, and gave rise to the study of many problems which had previously lagged behind the general development of science. Without troubling to make a full study of the basic notions of this new form of analysis, many scientists competed in a race for results which, because of the issuing of many challenges, had become even more heated. Within a matter of some ten years there appeared a host of new results based on individual research or on polemics, but without any general plan. In this somewhat anarchic crop, the more important discoveries were drowned in a mass of uninteresting results. Nevertheless, in 1730, Euler began his work of painstaking and methodical systematization. He soon managed to correlate the general results obtained, and to turn them into a much more solid body of doctrine from which there emerged some important concepts, soon to lead to new developments. Thus this host of results played a decisive role in the genesis of the infinitesimal calculus.

In the domain of mathematics and in that of the theoretical sciences, many similar examples can be cited. This is also the case in the observational and experimental sciences, where the emergence of a new concept, the invention of a new technique or of a new instrument, is very often the cause of a brilliant series of discoveries.

Telescopes and Microscopes

In all discoveries connected with observational science, instruments evidently play a role of the first importance. If there are many instances of theoretical discoveries leading to the design and the construction of new observational or measuring instruments, the examples of scientific discoveries resulting from the use of new, more powerful, or more perfect instruments are even more common. The many discoveries that followed close on the heels of the invention of the astronomical telescope and the microscope are particularly striking in this connection.

We know that very imperfect glass lenses had been in common use since the fifteenth century for correcting faulty vision, and it is clear that sooner or later work on these lenses was bound to lead to the construction of apparatus similar to the astronomical telescope or to the compound microscope. Relatively little is known about the exact circumstances of the actual invention of these instruments; it seems that it was only at the beginning of the seventeenth century that Dutch lens makers managed to demonstrate the importance of such instruments for observing distant or very small objects.

The reasons for such a delay are manifold. First of all there were technical reasons arising out of the poor quality of the glass used, bad cutting, and various aberrations interfering with the clarity and the definition of the image. Then there were philosophic reasons. Physicists would not consider lenses to be scientific instruments, and scholastic philosophers refused to concern themselves with the false appearances and wrong images produced by them. Thus it can be easily understood that it was to a scientist who, from the very outset of his work, had dared to undermine the edifice of ancient philosophy, to Galileo, that we owe the first use of this instrument for scientific purposes. In 1609, when Galileo started the construction of his first telescope, this instrument was already known in Holland, in France and in Italy. However, it was only being used for the observation of distant terrestrial objects. In 1610 Galileo took the courageous step, almost characteristic of his genius, of observing celestial phenomena with a telescope that he himself had constructed, and which he had installed in the garden of his house in Padua (*see* Plate II). His success was immediate, and we may say without exaggeration that the beginnings of modern astronomy date from that day. In very rapid succession this achievement was followed by other significant discoveries, providing against Aristotle's cosmological conception and Ptolemy's geocentric system new arguments that are still held by most contemporary scientists. Such were the discovery of the first four satellites of Jupiter, illustrating a planetary system similar to the Solar system and leading to the heliocentric hypothesis of Copernicus; of the irregularities of the lunar surface (figs. 1, 2 and 3) and of the existence of spots on the surface of the Sun which destroyed Aristotle's theory of the incorruptibility of the Heavens; the observation of the phases of Venus which brought to nought one of the chief arguments of the adversaries of Copernicus; the examination of the Milky Way which showed that it consisted of a multitude of stars while Aristotle had classified it as a meteor.

True, Galileo has no monopoly of these astronomical observations, and his prior claim to some of them has been disputed, but it was he alone who seized upon the full theoretical importance of these new discoveries. The timely publication of these first observations in his *Sidereus Nuncius* of 1610 aroused both great controversy and also ardent support.

In various countries amateurs began to examine the sky in order to verify Galileo's observations and to make further discoveries. Soon the satellites of Jupiter were identified separately. Peiresc was the first to discover a nebula, namely that in Orion, and he made his first discoveries in broad daylight; Bouilliau made an accurate study of the variations in luminosity of the variable star *Mira Ceti* in the constellation of Cetus; Gassendi observed the passage of Mercury across the Sun, while the English amateur Horrocks followed the passage of Venus. Various amateur astronomers observed the phases of Mercury, the bands of Jupiter, the spots of Mars, or added to our knowledge of lunar topography (Plate I).

But telescopes were still very imperfect. Not only was their magnification weak, but also they were awkward to handle and suffered particularly from optical faults. Thus the limit of their possibilities was rapidly reached, and some ten years later most of the phenomena observable with these rudimentary instruments had been discovered. Further decisive advances were not made until there were further improvements, viz. Huygens' improvement in the construction of the telescope, technical advances in the production of lenses, the adaptation of the telescope to classical astronomical instruments, the use of the micrometer, and the use of pendulum clocks. The erection of modern observatories has also contributed to progress, but this belongs to a later period, starting in about 1670, viz. the birth of precision astronomy which we shall not study here.[1]

While the astronomical telescope, by increasing the possibilities of celestial observation tremendously, heralded the developments of astronomy, microscopes which appeared at the same time led to the observation and study of phenomena on a scale that was much too small to be observed with the naked eye. In 1615 Galileo used the microscope for the observation of very small insects, and from then onwards this instrument has been very successful. The account by the erudite Claude Fabri de Peiresc (1580–1637) of his observa-

[1] A comparison of Figs. 1–3 (drawings of the Moon made by Galileo in 1610) with Plate I (drawing of the Moon by C. Mellan, 1636) and with Plate IV (a modern photograph of a lunar region) will bring out the importance of the advances in knowledge about our satellite. A comparison of Plate II (astronomical telescope used by Galileo) with Plate III (the 200″ telescope of the Palomar Mountain Observatory) clearly illustrates the advances in the techniques of astronomical observation.

tions in Paris in 1682, with a new instrument, demonstrate its picturesque rather than its scientific character.[1]

The first microscopic drawings that were published were drawings of bees by F. Stelluti, appearing in the *Apiarum* of Cesi (1625) (Plate V).[2] These drawings are very accurate, but they could probably have been made equally well with a very powerful single lens. In fact the serious optical faults of the microscopes of that time were much more pronounced than the corresponding faults of astronomical telescopes, where the bad quality of the image was not such a handicap.

Many amateurs continued to prefer simpler microscopes, i.e. somewhat better lenses.[3]

It was only in the second part of the seventeenth century that improvements in the production of the compound microscope, and increases in the magnifying power of the simple microscope, led to the demonstration of the first consequences of this invention. Within a few years there appeared a host of new observations, described in the *Micrographia* of the English physicist Robert Hooke (Plate VI), in the *Historia Insectorum generalis* of the Dutch biologist Swammerdam, in the papers published from 1671 onwards by the Italian Malpighi (Plate VII), and in the different publications of the great Dutch microscopist and biologist Leeuwenhoek. The observation of vegetable and animal cells and the beginnings of histology, the discovery of infusoria and the first steps in microbiology, the study of the structure of various organs, the observation of the capillaries and the circulation of the blood, and the discovery of spermatozoa (Plate IX) are some of the principal discoveries which were made almost immediately after the microscope was first used, and which transformed important sections of anatomy and of plant and animal physiology.[4]

---

[1] P. Humbert, 'Peiresc et le microscope' (*Rev. Hist. Sc.*, Vol. IV, 1951).

[2] Ch. Singer: 'The first microscopic discoveries' (*Endeavour*, Vol. XII, 1953).

[3] For a detailed study of this problem, cf. M. Daumas, *Les Instruments scientifiques aux XVIIe et XVIIIe siècles*, Paris, P.U.F., 1953.

[4] A comparison of Plates VII and VIII (drawings of plant sections by Malpighi, 1675; photograph of onion cells made with the ultramicroscope) with Plates IX, X and XI (first drawings of spermatozoa, photographs of spermatozoa with phase contrast and electron microscopes) will give us an appreciation of the skill (and sometimes the over-keen imagination) of the first observers, and also of the importance of the advances in the techniques of microscopic observation.

This rapid series of first successes of the two instruments discovered at the same time, each increasing the possibilities of vision in opposite directions, had two essential objects: to demonstrate by means of particularly striking examples the primary role of instruments in all discoveries in the field of the observational sciences, and to show how at certain epochs the impetus of a new invention has led to a whole series of quite different further discoveries within a matter of years. Such examples of 'associated discoveries' occur in the history of science quite often, for as soon as an invention or a discovery of any importance, or a somewhat spectacular hypothesis, concept or method opens up new paths to science, many research workers will abandon their previous work and will be attracted to these new fields, into which they enter in the hope of gathering a new harvest of facts more quickly than they could have done elsewhere.

CHAIN DISCOVERIES

But the fruitful influence of an invention can equally appear in the form of a chain of discoveries of which each link is the more or less logical consequences of the preceding, and the cause of the subsequent one.

From Cathode Rays to Radium

A particularly striking example of this type of discovery is found in the consequences of the discovery of X-rays by the German physicist Wilhelm Conrad Röntgen (1845–1923) in November 1895, in his laboratory at Würzburg.

We shall first give a brief account of this discovery itself. Röntgen had long been interested in the cathode rays emitted by evacuated tubes, and while observing the flow of current in a Crookes's tube covered with black cardboard, he noticed the appearance of very clearly defined fluorescence on a screen of barium platinocyanide placed on the experimental table.[1] Surprised by this unexpected phenomenon, Röntgen made further experiments

[1] Other investigators, such as Crookes, had already noticed similar phenomena, but without attaching any importance to them. It is Röntgen's essential merit that he appreciated the full importance of this unexpected phenomenon.

which established quite definitely that this fluorescence was caused by mysterious rays which, coming from the tube, had crossed the screen of black paper, despite the fact that this paper was opaque to all known forms of light. He then made a systematic study of this new radiation which, although invisible, could affect photographic plates and produce fluorescence in some substances, and which had a previously unheard-of power of penetration. At the time he could not specify the nature of this radiation, and therefore gave it the name of X-rays. These new rays caused conductivity in the gases through which they passed, discharged electrified bodies, were not deviated by electrical fields, and seemed to be propagated in a straight line similar to light, but without the classical phenomena of reflection, refraction and diffraction. However, the most astonishing property of X-rays was unquestionably their extraordinary power of penetration, varying with the nature of the body through which they passed. In the course of one of his experiments, Röntgen observed that the rays crossed his hand and that owing to the difference in transparency between bones and flesh he could obtain an image of the bone structure, and also of the contours of the opaque flesh, on a screen or a photographic plate.

The new possibilities of photographing the invisible were so astonishing that the new discovery very quickly took root both amongst the public at large and amongst scientific circles, arousing intense curiosity in both. Scientists were particularly interested since Röntgen's experiments were very easily repeated by means of very simple material found in all electrical laboratories. Thus on the 20th January, 1896, Drs. Oudin and Barthélemy were able to submit a 'photograph of the bones of the hand taken by means of Prof. Röntgen's X-rays' to the Paris Académie des Sciences (see Plate XII).

While a great number of experiments led to an ever-increasing concern for applying X-rays to human pathology, and particularly to surgical diagnosis, physicists were busy with determining the precise conditions for producing the new rays and with investigating their properties. Röntgen himself demonstrated that X-rays are produced whenever a beam of cathode rays meets a solid obstacle, gave evidence of the influence of the degree of rarefaction of the gas contained in the generating tube on the properties of the

X-rays generated, and made the first experiments on the reflection of the rays. In the meantime many other physicists discovered various properties of this mysterious radiation which seemed to be very similar to that produced by light rays.

Here we shall merely consider the most immediate consequences. We shall not emphasize either Von Laue's elegant experiment of diffraction by crystal gratings in 1912 which definitely established the wave-nature of X-rays, Bragg's reflection experiment, the study of the spectra of the rays which led to the enunciation of Moseley's Law (1913), or the study of the corpuscular properties of these new rays. However, we must mention the most important discovery of radioactivity which, although its principles were certainly quite independent of X-rays, is nevertheless a direct consequence of Röntgen's discovery. The factual connection between these two discoveries will serve to illustrate the creative potentialities unleashed by some hypotheses, even if they are partially incorrect.

It was Henri Poincaré who, on the 20th January, 1896, presented to the *Académie des Sciences* the radiographic negatives of Oudin and Barthélemy, and also the first details of Röntgen's discovery. He particularly stressed the fact that in the still very rudimentary equipment used by the German physicist, X-rays appeared where the cathode rays emitted by the Crookes's tube hit the wall of the tube. Since the glass of the tube was found to be fluorescent in that region under the effect of the cathode rays, Poincaré assumed that the two phenomena of fluorescence and of the emission of X-rays were interconnected. In fact this assumption was erroneous. Later observations showed that the two phenomena were independent of each other—but Poincaré's assumption had the great merit of leading to a discovery of incalculable scope, that of radioactivity.

An old fellow-pupil of Poincaré at the *École Polytechnique* and a member of the *Académie des Sciences*, Henri Becquerel (1852–1908), lecturer at the *Museum*, and following in the footsteps of his father, Edmund Becquerel (1820–1891), had been keenly concerned with the very marked phosphorescence of uranium compounds. Thus he was directly interested in Poincaré's remarks and, at the suggestion of this great physicist and mathematician, he began systematic research on the question whether some bodies that fluoresced or phosphoresced after previous exposure to light did not also emit

PLATE V

DETAIL IN A PLATE BY FRANCESCO STELLUTI (1577–1640), FROM THE *Apiarum* OF FEDERICO CESI (1585–1630). THIS WORK CONTAINS THE OLDEST KNOWN DRAWINGS OF OBJECTS SEEN THROUGH A MICROSCOPE

The plate is dedicated to 'His Holiness Urban VIII, as a token of my undying devotion'. (Urban VIII was a member of the Barberini family, whose coat of arms bore three bees.) Thus, just as Galileo's Siderius Nuncius was dedicated to the Medici, this first book of microscope drawings was also dedicated to a powerful Italian family. This rare work is much sought after by collectors.

PLATE VI

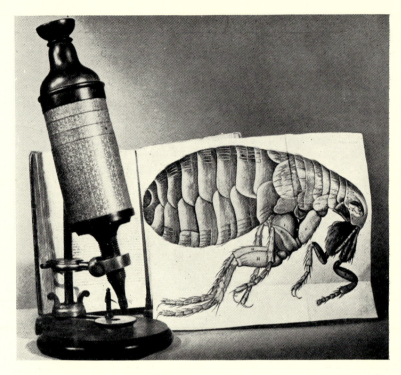

MODEL OF ROBERT HOOKE'S MICROSCOPE IN FRONT OF HIS *Micrographia* . . .
(London, 1655), OPENED AT PLATE XXXIV, A DRAWING OF THE FLEA

The body of Hooke's microscope was made up of four cardboard tubes fitting into one another. The objective, a biconvex lens of very small focal length, was held in an externally threaded wooden holder by means of a very small diaphragm. The apparatus was focussed by turning the thread in a ring attached to the support. The eyepiece, consisting of a planoconvex and a small biconvex lens, was mounted on another wooden holder, fitting over the first of the cardboard tubes. The apparatus could be moved vertically and also rotated. Its magnification was of the order of × 30.

The Micrographia *is a beautiful folio, containing 60 microscopic and three telescopic drawings. It is here shown opened at page 210, at the description of Observation LIII: 'Of a Flea'. The facing plate, XXXIV (17″ × 14″), is one of the best and largest of the whole collection. The drawing is very clear and the caption reads:* 'The strength and beauty of this small creature, had it no other relation at all to man, would deserve a description.'

PLATE VII

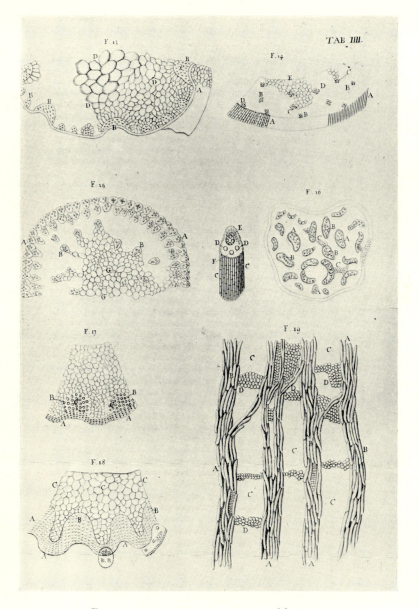

DRAWINGS OF BOTANICAL SECTIONS BY MALPIGHI

much reduced in scale, from *Anatome plantarum*. . . . London, 1675,
Part I, Plate IV

The cells are drawn very accurately. The author called them saccules *or* utricles,
*but did not appreciate their importance. The theory of cells was not born until the
first half of the nineteenth century.*

PLATE VIII

ULTRAMICROSCOPE-PHOTOGRAPH OF THE ONION CELL

The nucleus is in the centre, and the cytoplasm at the periphery
(after Wyckoff and Rozsa).

radiation similar to that of X-rays produced in Crookes's tubes. Poincaré developed this idea in an article in the *Revue Génerale des Sciences* on the 20th January, 1896. The article was devoted to the problem of invisible photography, and Poincaré's contribution appeared side by side with that of Röntgen, and that of the very young physicist Jean Perrin who, at the time, was preparing for his doctorate.

Excited by this experimental project which might shed new light on the phenomena of phosphorescence which he had studied for so long, Henri Becquerel first investigated crystals of the double sulphate of potassium and uranium of which he had a vast collection. In his first experiments, he exposed to sunlight for four hours photographic plates carefully shielded from the light by thick black sheets of paper on which he had placed a grain of the uranium salt. Upon developing the plates on the same day, he was pleased to discover that an outline of the grain of the phosphorescent salt had appeared in the form of a dark smudge. Poincaré's hypothesis was apparently verified: the salt had emitted a radiation which, like X-rays, could affect a photographic plate across a screen that is opaque to light. Becquerel announced his first discovery on the 24th February, 1896.

A few days later, while making further experiments with improved arrangements, he took out those plates which he was going to use. These plates had been kept in a dark drawer in the immediate proximity of the uranium crystals. Since they had not previously been exposed to light this factor was apparently irrelevant to the subsequent experiments. Nevertheless, owing to scruples typical of his strict experimental method, Becquerel decided to make sure first of all whether the plates were perfectly intact. For this purpose he developed one of them and was astonished to observe the outlines of the uranium sulphate crystals. He then decided to repeat the experiment by placing some uranium salt next to a photographic plate away from all light. The result was conclusive and showed that, without being exposed to the rays of the Sun, the crystals had emitted a radiation which, crossing sheets of paper, plates of glass and even aluminium, could affect photographic plates. Without waiting to get to the source of this phenomenon, discovered on the 2nd March, Becquerel communicated the result

E

of his experiments to the *Académie des Sciences*. He was then fully convinced that he had discovered a property of exceptional importance that was soon to revolutionize classical physics; i.e. natural radioactivity. Becquerel then made a deeper study of this phenomenon and tried to fathom its consequences, which, in fact, turned out to be much more far-reaching than he could have suspected. He soon discovered that no previous luminous excitation however far removed in time was involved, and found that there was no decrease in activity as a function of time. He also verified that many other uranium salts could be used for the experiment with equal effect, a fact which soon led him to suppose that this is a property characteristic of the element uranium, and not related, as he had first thought, to the phenomenon of phosphorescence. Nevertheless Becquerel still remained convinced that this 'uranic radiation' was identical with X-rays. His subsequent discoveries that 'uranic radiation' could render the air conductive, discharging those electrified bodies that it acted upon, could but reassure this eminent physicist, at least provisionally, that he was correct in his idea.

Soon afterwards many research workers made a careful analysis of the nature of this new radiation. The study of its composition, of its behaviour in a magnetic field and of its absorption, clearly demonstrated its complex nature, but it was not until after the discovery of new elements (and particularly of radium, an element producing far greater intensity of radiation than uranium) that its three constituents could be isolated, studied and identified. This achievement is mainly due to the English physicist Ernest Rutherford (1871–1937), to Becquerel, and to Pierre and Marie Curie in the course of research work lasting from 1897 to 1903. Rutherford designated the three radiations in growing order of their penetrating power by the Greek letters alpha, beta and gamma.

Towards the end of 1897, at the instigation of Becquerel, new research work was undertaken by the talented young physicist Pierre Curie (1859–1906), lecturer at the *Ecole de Physique et Chemie*, and by his young wife Marie Curie (1867–1934), to investigate whether this property of emitting the new radiation was characteristic of uranium alone, or if it also operated in other chemical elements. This involved a systematic study of the radiation possibilities of the principal known substances. Tackling this work under her husband's guidance, Marie Curie first made a most meticulous study of the characteristics of this property, carefully distinguishing it from other phenomena with very similar characteristics. She then showed how this activity could be measured by the degree of conductivity that it induced in the air. Her subsequent systematic research work led to her being able to demonstrate the existence of another element which, like uranium, also emitted radiation, namely thorium, and thus to her supplanting the now erroneous expression 'uranic radiation' with the word 'radioactivity', a phenomenon which was to become of increasing importance. Some months later she made the further and much more brilliant discoveries of the two new elements polonium and radium, whose radioactivity was respectively many hundred and many million times that of uranium.

Without entering here into the details of these significant discoveries which, in their turn, opened up immense new horizons to science both in the theoretical and in the applied sphere, we shall merely note some points which we consider essential aspects of the methodology of scientific research.

To begin with, it is incontestable that the discovery of radium and polonium led to that of radioactivity, and that this development can be considered as due both to logical and also to factual reasons. Furthermore, the isolation of these two elements, existing as they do in very small proportions in even the richest ores, could not have been effected without making use of their radioactive properties.

Although it is well known, it is perhaps not useless to recall the starting point of the research work which led Pierre and Marie Curie to the isolation of these two new elements. This is, in fact, a particularly brilliant example of the essential role which systematic observation plays in scientific discovery, once a sufficiently discerning mind knows how to take advantage of what are apparently discrepancies that a more superficial observer might have overlooked. In the course of her systematic investigation of all substances having radioactive properties, Marie Curie noticed that certain compounds of uranium, viz. the oxide (pitchblende) and a double phosphate of uranium and copper (chalcolite), were very much more intensely radioactive than their uranium and thorium content would have led one to suppose. Marie Curie fully realized the importance of this fact, which she interpreted courageously and shrewdly.

'This fact,' she pointed out in a note to the *Académie des Sciences*, 'is very remarkable and leads one to believe that these minerals may contain an element that is much more active than uranium.'

The accuracy of this hypothesis was to lead Pierre and Marie Curie to the discovery of radium, but a great deal of perseverance was still needed. Not knowing any of the chemical properties of the substance to be isolated, the two scientists concentrated their attention on its only observable property, radioactivity. Thus they devised a method of separation which, within twenty years, was to lead to the identification of all the other natural radioactive elements. This method consisted of applying every known physical and chemical means for separating different elements to the very complex minerals contained in pitchblende, and then of conserving those fractions that were most radioactive. Thus they could progressively enrich the radioactivity of two solutions by means of the fractionation of the original mineral. The first of these solutions, which showed characteristic traces of bismuth, allowed them to tackle the preparation of a new simple radioactive element called polonium (1898) in honour of Marie Curie's country of birth. The second fraction, containing barium, also showed intense radioactivity and its spectroscopic analysis revealed the presence of another new element—radium (26th December, 1898), of which Pierre and Marie Curie managed to isolate some decigrams in the form of the chloride. This was many million times more radioactive than uranium. Although its preparation, particularly in the beginning, had been very arduous and complicated, its radioactive properties were so intense that many consequences of radioactivity that had previously been unobserved could now be demonstrated easily. Having at their disposal this much more powerful source, physicists could now begin to elucidate the mechanism of radioactivity, and thus revise their concept of the constitution of matter.

We must insist on another point, namely the exceptional determination, the self-denial and the courageous patience which these two scientists brought to bear on the very delicate and difficult operations of separation under exceptionally precarious material conditions, and with very expensive apparatus. In order to obtain some decigrams of pure chloride of radium they had had to treat two tons of pitchblende, and to make thousands of operations and measurements. However, to their courage and confidence in success which made them persevere in their very often unrewarding tasks, the Curies added a very keen sense of method and scientific strictness. Furthermore, by uniting their efforts, they increased their chances of success, since their research work involved a profound knowledge of very different physical and chemical methods, and here their individual training, mental orientations and tendencies very fortunately supplemented one another. Their achievement not only crowned their genius and courage, but it also stressed the ever more imperative need for the collaboration between research workers with different specialities and scientific backgrounds.

We have here restricted our attention to the two most essential discoveries which derived directly from the observation of X-rays by Röntgen. It cannot be denied that this discovery contributed to a revision of all the most important chapters of physics and chemistry. But other and quite independent factors have equally contributed to this revolution which took place at the end of the nineteenth century. However, in extending our study further, we should seriously risk limiting its scope.

The main fact which we have wished to illustrate is the effective connection between these three striking discoveries. If the separation of radium imperatively required the prior demonstration of radioactivity in an already known substance, the discovery of this latter phenomenon was by no means the logical consequence of the discovery of X-rays. The artificially logical connection between these two facts was introduced not by the true nature of the facts, but by Poincaré's inaccurate hypothesis. Thus we have yet another extremely convincing example of error as a source of discoveries to add to our previous list.

Before leaving this example, we must finally emphasize the part that unforeseen phenomena have played in these three discoveries; i.e. the appearance of fluorescent spots on Röntgen's screen, the appearance of the image of uranium-salt crystals on the plates stored in Becquerel's drawer, the observation of abnormal radioactivity of some uranium minerals by Marie Curie. However, in none of these cases was it accidental and trivial effects, but observations made by research workers trying to pay attention to all aspects of reality as paradoxical as they might appear, that led to the investigations. In every case the investigator, by strict and fruitful scientific procedure, knew how to give an adequate interpretation so that his discovery could become a part of science. In this respect there are perhaps few better examples of the scientific method applied with strictness and perspicacity.

MORE COMPLEX CHAINS

Spectrum Analysis

The history of spectrum analysis will provide us with a modern example of the very much more complex interdependence between links in the chain of one and the same discovery. The observation of the colours of the rainbow and the subsequent observation of the dispersive effect of a refractive prism were the basis of many theories. But it was only with Descartes, Newton and Euler that there arose a clear understanding of the similarity between the two phenomena, since the assumption of the complex nature of natural light presupposes a systematic study of the phenomena of dispersion.

In 1802, looking through a prism at a slit strongly illuminated by the Sun, the English physicist Wollaston observed dark lines on the solar spectrum. Unable to explain this phenomenon, he gave up its investigation, thus narrowly missing an important discovery. A little later, in 1815, the German physicist Joseph von Fraunhofer rediscovered this phenomenon in the course of his research work on the achromatic effects of a system of lenses and of prisms. By placing a collimator in front of a prism and behind a lens (and thus inventing the spectroscope), Fraunhofer managed to produce and identify accurately a whole series of narrow dark lines, which he denoted by letters and distinguished by their corresponding refractive indices. Thus a new technique, i.e. spectroscopy, was created, based on the study of the absorption spectrum of the Sun. However, subsequent progress was rather slow, although Fraunhofer, in designing the diffraction grating, had provided this new branch of physics with a very useful instrument.

During the succeeding years observations increased, but there was no coherent and satisfactory theory permitting their explanation and rational application. Fraunhofer noticed that the spectrum of an ordinary flame had no dark lines, but that a yellow line, the D line, could be seen in the very place where there was a sharp dark line in the solar spectrum. He also observed the existence of sharp lines in the spectrum of electric sparks. J. Herschel and Talbot in their turn noticed the existence of characteristic red lines in the spectrum of strontium salts. In 1835 Wheatstone observed that the lines of the spectrum of the electric arc depend on the nature of the electrodes, and in 1855 Angström showed that by lowering the pressure of the surrounding gas this influence of the electrodes could be eliminated, and the spectrum of the gas used could be obtained alone.

Many authors had made rather inexact assumptions about the origin of the dark absorption lines. The first scientist to explain this phenomenon was the Frenchman Foucault who, in 1849, experimented with the spectrum of an electric arc between iron electrodes. Unfortunately, Foucault restricted himself to the case of the D lines of sodium, and did not make a general study of the origin of absorption lines.

From 1855 onwards the wider use of Geissler tubes led to a rapid increase in observations of the spectra of rarefied gases.

Finally, in 1859, a fully satisfactory explanation was given by the German physicists Gustav Robert Kirchhoff (1824-1887) and Robert Wilhelm Bunsen (1841-1899) who showed that each line of the spectrum was due to the presence of a given element and conversely, that absorption was due to its presence in the Sun's atmosphere.[1] The value of this hypothesis was demonstrated by the discovery of two new elements, caesium and rubidium (1861).

From that time on, spectrum analysis could be considered as definitely established, and as its techniques became better and more perfect, so the experimental results and discoveries increased in rapid succession. Many physicists directed their research work towards this new field. New elements were still to be discovered (thallium by Crookes in 1861, indium by Reich and Richter in 1863, gallium by Lecocq de Boisbaudran in 1875, and helium—first

[1] For further details, cf. Georg Lockemann, *Robert Wilhelm Bunsen*, Stuttgart, 1949. *Grosse Naturforscher*, Vol. VI.

seen in the solar spectrum in 1866), and in 1864 Huggins managed to identify the principal lines of the solar spectrum. Many descriptive works now appeared characterizing and classifying the main types of spectra—viz., band spectra, flame spectra, arc spectra, and light-bulb spectra.[1] When Mendeleieff published his periodic classification of the elements in 1869, it was discovered that the spectrum of each element increased in complexity with the number assigned to it in this classification. The exact study of the hydrogen lines, already observed by Angström, endowed this fact with a very special significance. In 1885 the physicist Johann Jakob Balmer (1825–1898) managed to establish, in a purely experimental way, that those lines of the spectrum of that gas, which were known at that time, had wave-lengths which satisfied the equation

$$\lambda = h \; \frac{m^2}{m^2 - 4}$$ where the constant h is exactly equal to 3645·6A,

and where m is an integer greater than 2. Perhaps in the whole of physics there is no other formula, obtained empirically, whose exactness can be verified with such accuracy. Thus recent observations have led to demonstrations of lines corresponding to its thirty-first term. While in 1890 Rydberg extended this formula to other elements, in 1907 Ritz generalized the expression by means of his principle of combination. However, there appeared no truly satisfactory explanation of this law, which by its exactness and accuracy continued to puzzle and challenge the ingenuity of scientists for a great many years.

Speaking, in 1904, on 'The future of mathematical physics',[2] Henri Poincaré showed his full appreciation of the great importance which a solution of this problem would have.

'. . . Why are the spectra of the lines distributed according to a regular law? These laws have been studied by experimenters in their smallest details, they have been made precise and relatively simple. . . . This fact [i.e. their difference from those governing the vibra-

---

[1] We may note that many heated claims of priority followed the publication of Kirchhoff and Bunsen's work. These claims were made by Angström, by some French physicists in favour of Foucault, and by others in favour of Stokes, Alter, Talbot and Stewart. However, although it would appear that this discovery existed potentially in the minds of many physicists, the credit for it must belong to Kirchhoff and Bunsen, who alone expressed it in accurate and general terms.

[2] Lecture in St. Louis, 1904. Text printed in *La Valeur de la Science*.

PLATE IX

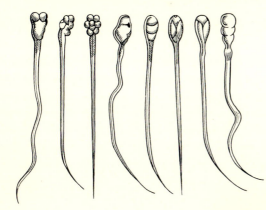

A. THE FIRST KNOWN DRAW-
INGS OF SPERMATOZOA OF
MAMMALS BY LEEUWENHOEK

*These drawings of the sper-
matozoa of the dog and the rabbit
were attached to Leeuwenhoek's
letter of the 18th March, 1678.*
(Philosophic Transactions,
1679.)

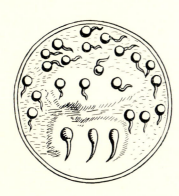

B. HUMAN SPERMATOZOA AFTER
SPALLANZANI

(*Opuscoli di fisica animale e vegetabile*,
vol. II, Modena 1776; *Le Opere di
Lazarro Spallanzani . . .*, Vol. III, p. 471,
Fig. 1.) The relevant text is on page 335
of the same volume.

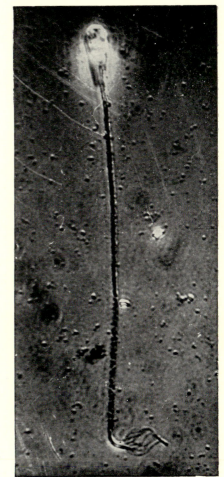

C. SPERMATOZOON SEEN IN VARICOLOUR
PHASE-CONTRAST

*The image of the head is poor, but the
terminal filaments can be clearly distinguished.*

This remarkable combination of photographs shows the great possibilities of the electron microscope. The complexity of the structures explains why the early microscopists found it so difficult to arrive at satisfactory explanations. The true role of the spermatozoon in fertilization was not understood properly until the second half of the nineteenth century.

The structure of the spermatozoon was explained partially by the recent work of Bretschneider and his collaborators at the Delft Institute of Electron Microscopy, and by the work of Reed and Saunders. By means of the electron microscope we can study objects between 0·2 microns (limit of the optical microscope) and 0·002 microns (size of the macromolecule), thus covering the field of biological functions which, as in the case of cell mobilities, depend on the action of molecular forces.

Invented in 1932, the electron microscope has already led to important advances in the study of macromolecular structures, and especially in animal and vegetable tissues and cells. The photograph of an onion cell (Plate VIII) is a further example of the great scope of this instrument.

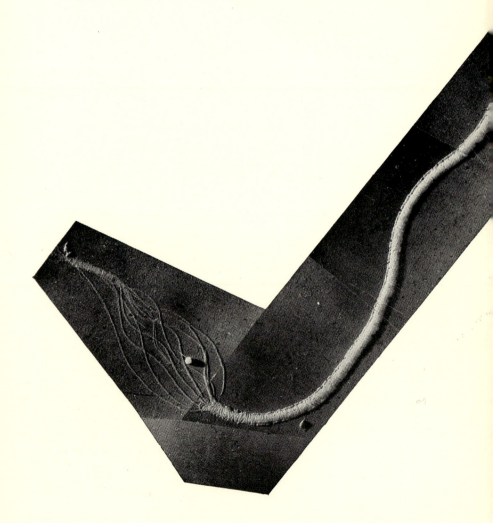

PLATE X

PLATE XI

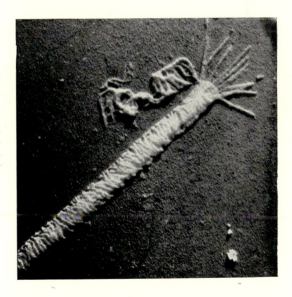

ELECTRON MICROSCOPE
PICTURE OF THE INTERNAL
FIBRILS OF THE CAUDAL
SHEATH OF A SPERMATO-
ZOON

PLATE XII

LA PHOTOGRAPHIE DE L'INVISIBLE

Par M. L. OLIVIER, Dʳ és sciences
Directeur de la *Revue générale des sciences.*

La nouvelle de la grande découverte que vient de faire le professeur Röntgen a passé directement de son laboratoire dans le public, où elle s'est propagée avec la rapidité de l'éclair avant même que les journaux scientiques aient eu le temps d'en parler.

Il n'est bruit, en ce moment, que des « rayons

A. THE HEADING OF THE FIRST ARTICLE ON THE DISCOVERY OF X-RAYS TO APPEAR IN A FRENCH MÉDICAL JOURNAL

(*La Presse médicale*, No. 6, 29th January, 1896.)

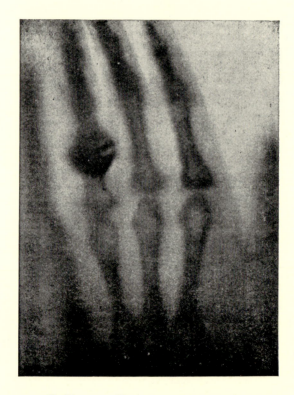

B. THE FIRST X-RAY PICTURE OF A HAND

Despite the poor quality of this picture (taken with very primitive apparatus) this first photograph of the 'invisible' aroused a tremendous amount of curiosity.

tions of an elastic body] has not been accounted for, and I believe that we have here one of the most important secrets of nature.'

Poincaré then mentioned the tentative explanation of the Japanese physicist Nagaoka, who considered the atom as consisting of a positive nucleus surrounded by a ring made up of a great number of very small electrons, and he suggested that this explanation should be taken into account. This path, which he had indicated so perspicaciously, proved to be particularly fruitful. In 1911 Rutherford deduced, from his experiments on the scattering of alpha rays, his famous hypothesis of the planetary structure of the atom, and two years later, in 1913, Niels Bohr laid the foundations for the application of quantum mechanics to the orbital movement of the electrons. Perfected by Sommerfeld in 1916, Bohr's theory of the atom led to a very satisfactory explanation of Balmer's law of the lines of hydrogen. But as often happens in the history of science, this explanation was not really convincing except for relatively simple cases. The creation of wave mechanics by Louis de Broglie and the later advances in atomic physics produced a considerable extension in its powers of explanation. Nevertheless, as in Poincaré's times, spectrum analysis continues to bring out problems whose solution would lead to new and important advances in our modern knowledge of the atom.

Thus did the observation of the absorption spectrum of the Sun by Wollaston and Fraunhofer mark the beginning of an uninterrupted series of experimental research work and of theories leading to innumerable discoveries which, together with other trends in research, have most fruitfully contributed to the creation of new branches of science, viz. atomic physics, nuclear physics and astrophysics. What is perhaps most characteristic of this long effort is that in it experiments came first and gave an impetus to the labours of theoreticians, contributing finally to the whole progress of atomic science. However, theory must follow very close on the heels of the evolution of experimental science, for else it would not be able to give a correct interpretation or lead to correct applications of results obtained by the latter. Many efforts would be dissipated and would lose part of their interest. Such was particularly the case with a great deal of the research work prior to the discoveries of Kirchhoff and Bunsen.

CHAPTER VI

FLASHES OF THOUGHT

THE study of various types of invention and discovery has shown us that after a long effort of reflection and research a discovery will suddenly flash into the mind of the research worker by means of a sudden illumination, the so-called *Geistesblitz*. The account of the discovery of Fuchsian functions by Poincaré has given us some striking examples of this. Two other examples equally deserve our consideration, viz. the more or less legendary story of the discovery of Archimedes' principle, and the precise and authentic account of Charles Nicolle's discovery of the transmission of typhus by fleas.

ARCHIMEDES' 'EUREKA'

It is to the great Roman architect Vitruvius, who lived during the reign of Augustus, about the beginning of the Christian Era, that we owe the account of Archimedes' discovery of his famous principle of floating bodies. Since it was written two centuries after the event, this description must evidently be treated with reserve. Nevertheless, even should it not be in perfect agreement with historical truth, it is certainly based on partially correct traditional accounts. This is borne out by the fact that the famous treatise *De Corporibus fluitantibus, libri duo,* in which Archimedes expounds the basis of scientific hydrostatics, contains some evidence agreeing with Vitruvius' account. The problems treated in this book are of the kind that we meet in elementary textbooks of applied mathematics, where the problem of calculating the specific gravity of the components of a mixture or compound is treated. According to Archimedes' principle the specific gravity of every component is inversely proportional to the volume of water it displaces. Vitruvius' account not only describes the sudden flash of discovery, but also the methodical work which permitted its applications.

'Of the great number of admirable discoveries made by Archimedes, we must stress that of which I am going to speak and in which he displayed an almost incredible subtlety of mind. When Hieron reigned over Syracuse, this prince, being fortunately blessed in all his enterprises, vowed a temple-offering to the immortal gods of a crown of gold. He agreed with a craftsman what sum should go into its making and weighed it out in gold. This artisan delivered his work to the King on the appointed day, who found it executed perfectly well. On weighing the crown it appeared to be of the same weight as the gold that had been issued; but a test suggested that the worker had retained a part of the gold, which he had replaced with silver in the crown.

'The King was very irate at being tricked in this way, but lacking the means of convicting the worker of theft, he asked Archimedes to devise one. Archimedes, while wholly absorbed in this matter, took a bath one day, and noticed that as he immersed himself in the tub, the water spilled over. This observation led him to the desired discovery, and he was so overcome by joy that he rushed out of the bath and, running naked through the house, he began shouting that he had discovered what he had sought, which in Greek is *Eureka, Eureka* (I have found it, I have found it). It is said that upon this discovery, he ordered two masses of the same weight as the crown, one of gold and one of silver, which he then plunged into a vessel of water. The immersion of the silver mass caused a quantity of water to overflow, equal to the volume of the silver. He then removed the latter, refilled the vessel with as much water as had overflowed, which gave him the quantity of water corresponding to the mass of silver that he had plunged into the vessel. After this experiment he similarly plunged a mass of gold into the same vessel of water, and after taking it out, he again measured the water which had spilled over. He found that the mass of gold had not caused as much water to overflow, and that the difference was equal to the difference between the volume of the mass of gold and that of an equal mass of silver. He then refilled the vessel, and this time plunged the crown into it, which caused more water to overflow than had the equal mass of gold, and less than the equal mass of silver. After these experiments he finally calculated how much more water the crown had caused to spill than the mass of gold had done, and he knew how much silver had been mixed with the gold. He then disclosed that the worker had clearly been a swindler.'[1]

[1] *The Architecture of Vitruvius*, Perrault's translation, Paris, 1936, Vol. II, pp. 169–77. *See also* Brunet and Mieli: *Histoire des Sciences. Antiquité*, Paris, Payot, 1935. Plate XIII is a naïve illustration of this story, drawn by a sixteenth-century artist.

THE MECHANISM OF THE TRANSMISSION OF TYPHUS

Our second example has much better guarantees of being authentic. It is in fact Charles Nicolle's own account of his discovery of the transmission of typhus by fleas, a discovery which he made in Tunis in 1909, and which he relates in his *Biologie de l'Invention*[1] as a typical example of a sudden flash of creative illumination. Any further comment is unnecessary, in view of the accuracy and the importance of his evidence.

'This shock, this sudden illumination, this instantaneous self-certainty of a new fact—I know of it, I have experienced it in my own life. It is in this way that the mode of transmission of ex-anthematic typhus was revealed to me. Like all those who for many years frequented the Moslem hospital of Tunis, I could daily observe typhus patients bedded next to patients suffering from the most diverse complaints. Like those before me, I was the daily and unhappy witness of the strange fact, that this lack of segregation, although inexcusable in the case of so contagious a disease, was nevertheless not followed by infection. Those next to the bed of a typhus patient did not contract the disease, while, almost daily, during epidemic outbreaks, I would diagnose contagion in the douars (the Arab quarters of the town), and amongst hospital staff dealing with the *reception* of patients. Doctors and nurses became contaminated in the country, in Tunis, but never in the hospital wards.

'One day, just like any other, immersed no doubt in the puzzle of the process of contagion in typhus, in any case not thinking of it consciously (of this I am quite sure), I entered the doors of the hospital, when a body at the bottom of the passage arrested my attention.

'It was a customary spectacle to see poor natives, suffering from typhus, delirious and febrile as they were, gain the landing and collapse on the last steps. As always I strode over the prostrate body. It was at this very moment that the light struck me. When, a moment later, I entered the hospital, I had solved the problem. I knew beyond all possible doubt that this was it. This prostrate body, and the door in front of which he had fallen, had suddenly shown me

[1] Paris, Alcan, 1932.

the barrier by which typhus had been arrested. For it to have been arrested, and, contagious as it was in entire regions of the country and in Tunis, for it to have remained harmless once the patient had passed the Reception Office, the agent of infection must have been arrested at this point. Now, what passed through this point? The patient had already been stripped of his clothing and of his underwear; he had been shaved and washed. It was therefore something outside himself, something that he carried on himself, in his underwear, or on his skin, which caused the infection. This could be nothing but a flea. Indeed, it was a flea. The fact that I had ignored this point, that all those who had been observing typhus from the beginnings of history (for it belongs to the most ancient ages of humanity) had failed to notice the incontrovertible and immediately fruitful solution of the method of transmission, had suddenly been revealed to me. I feel somewhat embarrassed about thus putting myself into the picture. If I do so, nevertheless it is because I believe what happened to me is a very edifying and clear example, such as I have failed to find in the case of others. I developed my observation with less timidity. At the time it still had many shortcomings. These, too, appear instructive to me.

'If this solution had come home to me with an intuition so sharp that it was almost foreign to me, or at least to my mind, my reason nevertheless told me that it required an experimental demonstration.

'Typhus is too serious a disease for experiments on human subjects. Fortunately, however, I knew of the sensitivity of monkeys. Experiments were therefore possible. Had this not been the case I should have published my discoveries without delay, since it was of such immediate benefit to everybody. However, because I could support the discovery with a demonstration, I guarded my secret for some weeks even from those close to me, and made the necessary attempts to verify it. This work neither excited nor surprised me, and was brought to its conclusion within two months.

'In the course of this very brief period I experienced what many other discoverers must undoubtedly have experienced also, viz. strange sentiments of the pointlessness of any demonstration, of complete detachment of the mind and of wearisome boredom. The evidence was so strong, that it was impossible for me to take any interest in the experiments. Had it been of no concern to anybody but myself, I well believe that I should not have pursued this course. It was because of vanity and self-love that I continued. Other thoughts occupied me as well. I confess this failing. It did not arrest my research work. The latter, as I have recounted, led easily and without a single day's delay to the confirmation of the truth, which I had known ever since that revealing event, of which I have spoken.'

CHAPTER VII

THE ROLE OF CHANCE

A CERTAIN number of examples of accidental observations leading
to fundamental discoveries has given credence to the opinion that
chance plays a primary role in scientific creation, and that many
discoveries would not have been made without the fortunate concurrence of very exceptional circumstances, without which any
efforts on the part of research workers would have remained
unfruitful or at least very unrewarding.

In actual fact, we must first of all distinguish between psychological chance, i.e. the fortuitous coming together of two ideas,
which, as it were, is a constant factor in every discovery, and
external chance, i.e. accidental facts which in some cases have led
research workers into particularly fruitful directions.

We shall delay our account of the role of psychological chance,
so clearly illustrated by Poincaré. This coming together of two ideas
opening the way for an invention is fortuitous in appearance only;
in fact it is prepared by a great deal of preliminary research work and
is fashioned by the intuition and aesthetic sense of the particular
research worker.

On the other hand is external chance, that exceptional concurrence of circumstances which may lead to a discovery, in fact as
frequent a phenomenon as some consider it to be? To judge this
question we must first of all eliminate a number of well-known
examples—and some less well-known and partially legendary
examples—where circumstances of not too exceptional a character
produce a mental flash in the mind of a scientist, deeply involved
in looking for the solution of a problem. Such is the case with the
celebrated anecdotes about Newton's apple, about Archimedes'
solution of the crown problem previously mentioned, and finally
that about the broken crystal which led Haüy to his crystallographic
theory. In all these cases the actual circumstances were by no means
exceptional, and it seems that even without them the discovery would
have appeared to the scientist's mind sooner or later, as long as his
mind was adequately prepared to consolidate it at the slightest shock.

We shall also disqualify observations of current phenomena whose frequency and regularity make study almost inevitable, and restrict ourselves to purely fortuitous observations, arising out of almost unpredictable coincidences which throw the research worker on to new paths that soon show their fruitfulness. It is here that we shall find true cases of the intervention of chance in discovery, while the other examples are nothing but more or less obvious manifestations of the role of the subconscious in research work.

TWO FAMOUS EXAMPLES

The example of Galvani's frog is well known. It was entirely by chance that the Italian Luigi Galvani observed that the calf muscles of a frog, suspended on a metallic support, contract under the effects of an electric spark produced in the neighbourhood. This phenomenon was actually very complex, and it might strike one as paradoxical that the production of an electric current should have made its first appearance in so hidden a form. However, chance was exploited by two scientists who had complementary talents—first by Galvani who was a very capable and versatile experimenter, and who carried out this experiment in different ways without being able to interpret it correctly, and then by Volta, a talented physicist whose prior training enabled him to give a rational interpretation of the observation, and who, by eliminating external factors, eventually invented the battery early in the year 1800 (*see* Plate XV).

An even better example is the discovery by the French mathematician Malus of the polarization of light by reflection. This young scientist was interested in the laws of geometrical optics, and particularly in the path of light rays in birefringent crystals. One day, while looking from his house in the rue d'Enfer at the sunlit windows of the Luxembourg Palace through a crystal of Iceland spar, he was surprised to observe that in turning the crystal about its axis each of the two images would vanish in turn. This fortuitous observation could not have fallen on a mind better prepared to draw the consequences. Malus realized that this phenomenon was connected with the reflection of the light by the windows, and he soon deduced the theory of polarization by reflection. This work attracted the attention of many physicists who made an analysis of other aspects of the same phenomenon, which Fresnel and Young managed to explain some years later by their theory of the transverse nature of light waves.

Another two fortuitous observations, analysed by scientists who were fully prepared to derive the greatest advantages from them, were the origins of two of the greatest discoveries at the beginning of the nineteenth century—the invention of the battery and the wave theory of light. Actually such clear examples occur but rarely, and our other examples of the intervention of chance will appear considerably more complex.

THE DISCOVERY OF SUB-CLINICAL CONDITIONS

In his highly personal, factual and thoughtful study, the *Biologie de l'Invention*, Charles Nicolle gives a very striking example of a discovery in which events and intuition have played complementary roles. This was the case with one of the most important discoveries of this great biologist, i.e. that of sub-clinical conditions, of which Georges Duhamel wrote that it seemed to him to be the 'most notable contribution of intelligence to the world'. In fact this new notion led to a better understanding of the evolution and trans-mission of infectious diseases, and in particular of some very surprising cases of contagion.

In the passage which we shall quote, Charles Nicolle shows clearly how some facts, discovered during his experimental study of typhus, led him to assume the existence of latent typhus, a restricted type of the disease which in the case of some patients had lost all its virulence, so much so that it could no longer be demonstrated otherwise than by the positive results of an inoculation of blood in a sensitive animal. Nicolle tried immediately to apply this concept to other diseases, and he was soon to be proved right. At the same time he was aware of the essential part which the latent condition could play in the transmission of the disease. Thus this discovery, which—at least in appearance—was the consequence of a simple fortuitous observation, assumed its full significance owing to the remarkable breadth and strictness of its author's mind, based always on observa-tion and methodical experiment. Charles Nicolle's account has the great merit of describing the circumstances and the successive phases of this discovery very accurately.

'We had just established that guinea-pigs were sensitive to ex-

F

anthematic typhus. Since the typhus agent could not be cultured, we had previously been forced to hold over our research work until the seasonal return of the Tunisian epidemics, when we could obtain the virus from human beings and preserve it for some weeks by passing it into monkeys, the only animal that we knew to be sensitive to it. The sensitivity of the guinea-pig, this useful animal, afforded us a convenient means for preserving the virus indefinitely by passing it into this species.

'Experimental typhus of the guinea-pig is a very minimal disease. It is reduced to small changes in the temperature curve, and could not be diagnosed without a thermometer, since the animal does not seem to suffer or to have any other symptoms.

'Now it happened occasionally that we discovered amongst our guinea-pigs, inoculated with the same virus, some who had no fever at all. The first time that we discovered this, we thought it was due to an accident in the inoculation or to the particular resistance of the inoculated animal. These were the two hypotheses by which all bacteriologists of that era would have explained this phenomenon.

'When the phenomenon kept recurring, we felt that our explanations had been too superficial, and that it must be due to another specific reason. We kept in mind the table of sensitivity to typhus of various races and species that we had observed or infected. At the top of the scale was the European adult who had immigrated to regions where typhus is endemic, and in whom the disease is most severe and often fatal. Below him appeared the aboriginal adult who is seriously infected but who, when there are no complications, generally escapes death. Then there comes the indigenous child for whom typhus, with few exceptions, is only a mild disease. Below our species there figures the chimpanzee, less sensitive still than the child, followed by even less sensitive small monkeys, and finally the guinea-pig whose infection is reduced to a thermometer curve. Could there not be below this hardly recognizable disease an even smaller degree of sensitivity, where, in the absence of fever, the only means of diagnosing typhus would be the positive results of an inoculation of blood into an animal of definite sensitivity? That this was the case was proved by experiment. Other experiments very soon proved to us that latent typhus, exceptional as it was in the case of guinea-pigs, was the only form of typhus in some other species.

'This latent typhus which we were the first to discover is a typhus of first infection. We were able to demonstrate the existence of the same sub-clinical type in other guinea-pigs, that had had primary typhus and were then reinoculated. The natural recurrence in man can also be of the sub-clinical type.

'Subsequently we, and others after us, extended the notion of latent infection to a number of bacterial infections. The list increases daily.

'Thus there exists a whole pathology that cannot be reached by clinical methods. If we add that it is in these unrecognizable forms that contagious and epidemic diseases are preserved, the practical importance of this new information is obvious. Now the starting-point of our discovery had been the simple absence of a temperature rise in some examples of a species which commonly becomes feverish after being inoculated with a virus.'

Actually the role of chance seems to be almost non-existent in this example. Charles Nicolle's observation of this absence of a temperature rise in some guinea-pigs that had been infected with typhus was in fact no accident but the discovery of one of the relatively rare forms of this disease. An attentive observer such as Charles Nicolle had to come across this somewhat exceptional form of typhus sooner or later.

What strikes us as most significant in this example, as in the case of many other discoveries, is on the one hand the part played by some abnormal forms of a well-known phenomenon (here the symptoms of typhus in the guinea-pig), and on the other hand its clear illustration of the initial mental effort which was at the very root of the discovery itself. The first observation of this abnormal phenomenon does not seem to have attracted Nicolle's attention directly, for he attributed it more or less consciously to an accident of inoculation or to the particular resistance of the inoculated animal. It was only when similar cases demonstrating the regularity of the phenomenon occurred, that he took an active interest in it. It was only then that the actual discovery was made, and that the intuitive powers, the intellectual courage and discipline of the scientist emerged most fruitfully. After he had understood this particular phenomenon clearly, it had still to be generalized by means of a long series of verifications, patient observations and experiments.

Thus the case of sub-clinical conditions may be considered as a typical example of discoveries which, arising out of accidental observations, are in fact the result of methodical intellectual work.

THE OPHTHALMOSCOPE

Another case of an unplanned invention, in which intuition and events played complementary parts, is that of the ophthalmoscope. Since it leads to an easy observation of the retina and to the differentiation between normal and pathological states in the back of the eye, the discovery of this instrument is at the root of many other advances in ophthalmology. The great German physiologist and physicist Hermann von Helmholtz (1821–1894) has given an account of the circumstances under which he made this invention in 1851:

'While preparing my lectures, I considered the possibility of constructing an ophthalmoscope . . . the ophthalmoscope is by far the most popular thing that I have done; but, in a manner of speaking, this invention has been due more to luck than to merit. I had to demonstrate to my pupils Brücke's theory of the illumination of the eye. In this, Brücke was within a hairsbreadth of the invention of the ophthalmoscope. He did not ask himself what optical images are produced by the rays that emerge from an eye into which a light is thrown. For his particular purposes it was not necessary to ask this question, but had it been posed, he would have been able to reply to it as quickly as I have.'[1]

Appreciating the principle of this new apparatus, Helmholtz tackled its construction. After a week of feverish effort he overcame the last obstacles, and by a combination of lenses and microscope slides he obtained an instrument that granted him 'the great joy of being the first person to see a living human retina clearly'.

We consider the example of this discovery to be a particularly striking one.

Helmholtz had obviously prepared the ground for this invention, both by his previous study and by his preoccupation at the time, and it is clear that the breadth of his knowledge, his daring ideas, and his experimental talents, brought the solution of this problem within his immediate reach. But it was still necessary that his mind take a

[1] As quoted by E. Claparède in 'L'invention dirigée' in L'invention, Alcan, 1938 (IXe Sem. Int. de Synth.).

direct interest in this question. If previously he had never dreamt of illuminating the retina of the living eye, at least he had been motivated more or less consciously by the desire of seeing what happens at the back of the eye, and as E. Claparède[1] suggests, we may take it that the examination of Brücke's paper could not have initiated in Helmholtz a mental desire or a need, but had shown him the way to realize the invention. This role of fortuitous circumstances is seen even more clearly if we compare the case of Helmholtz with that of Brücke who set him on his path. These two physiologists were of the same age, had followed parallel careers and were interested in the same problems. Brücke had studied the rays reflected by the surface of the retina for many years, and was particularly well qualified to invent the ophthalmoscope. Helmholtz's evidence confirms the fact that Brücke would not have missed this discovery had he himself posed that very problem. If we bear in mind the knowledge and the interests of these two physiologists, it becomes clear that the flash of thought which suddenly guided Helmholtz's research work could have occurred equally well in Brücke's case. Perhaps the only thing lacking was the fortuitous coincidence of the two ideas in Helmholtz's mind, or perhaps on the contrary it was the very definite orientation of Brücke's researches which prevented him from thinking of the right approach, that was as good as his for the asking.

THE DISCOVERY OF PENICILLIN

It is well known that one of the most important achievements of contemporary therapeutics is the discovery of antibiotics, due to the chance observations of the great English biologist Sir Alexander Fleming.

In the month of September 1928, Fleming, studying mutation in some colonies of staphylococci, noticed in the course of a microscopic examination that the plates of one of his cultures had been contaminated by a micro-organism from the air outside. Such a fact in itself was nothing but an insignificant accident, a small misadventure happening frequently to all research workers in laboratories with insufficient funds to take all the necessary precautions to prevent such contamination.

But instead of neglecting this incident and continuing his work

[1] *Ibid.*

on other preparations, Fleming went to the trouble of observing the contaminated plate in greater detail. It was then that he noticed a very surprising phenomenon: the colonies of staphylococci that had been attacked by microscopic fungi had become transparent in a large region around the initial zone of contamination (Plate XVII). Fleming thought that this effect could only be due to an antibacterial substance secreted by the foreign micro-organism and then spreading into the supporting medium of the preparation. He then decided to study more systematically the properties of this secretion with so strong an antibiotic effect. Thus more than 50 years after Tyndall, Pasteur and Joubert, who had made similar observations,[1] it was Fleming's turn to demonstrate the antibiotic effect of the secretion of a microscopic fungus (a variety of *penicillium*) on cultures of bacteria particularly sensitive to its action, viz. staphylococci (*see* Plate XVIIIA). But while the observations of his predecessors had no really important consequences, those of Fleming were followed up with patient research that led to the discovery of a particularly effective weapon against many bacterial infections.

Thus, departing from his plan of research, the English biologist began to study the principal properties of the anti-bacterial substance secreted by the fungi that had accidentally contaminated his plate. Employing the modest resources of his laboratory in the most versatile and effective way, he managed to demonstrate the selective properties of the substance and its action on different species of bacteria. Then, by injecting this substance into rabbits and mice, he showed that it did not affect the leucocytes of living organisms and proved that, even in very dilute solution, its anti-bacterial effects were still much superior to those of powerful antiseptics, such as carbolic acid. Eight months after his initial observations, Fleming published his observations in the *British Journal of Experimental Pathology*.[2]

This paper, which has today become a classic, was not given a very great reception on its first appearance. This is quite understandable because, even had Fleming fully realized the nature of the antibiotic that he had discovered, he could not have anticipated all its subsequent repercussions in the field of medicine. The liquid

---

[1] *La préhistoire des antibiotiques.*

[2] A. Fleming, 'On the antibacterial action of cultures of Penicillium with special reference to their use in the isolation of B influenzae' (*Brit. J. Exp. Path.*, Vol. X 1929).

secreted by the micro-organisms of *penicillium* was in fact difficult
to prepare, and its impurity and instability seemed to make any
practical application impossible. Physicians took little notice of
this new discovery, and only bacteriologists and biochemists were
interested in Fleming's results. A group of research workers at the
School of Hygiene and Tropical Medicine in London, consisting
of Dr. Harold Raistrik and his collaborators W. Clutterbuck and
R. Lovel, attempted to isolate the active principle contained in the
metabolic liquid secreted by the variety of *penicillium* investigated
by Fleming. While they managed to make a more precise chemical
study of this, their attempts to purify and preserve it were un-
successful, and in fact, an article of Raistrik in 1932, assessing his
experiments, announced that, for the time being at any rate, no
more work on the preparation of penicillin was to be done.

A further reason contributed equally to this provisional lack
of interest. In the ensuing years, the hopes of most physicians were
turned towards chemotherapy, which was then undergoing a
rapid evolution, and where new substances, soon to be known as
sulphanilamides, had just revealed anti-bacterial properties beyond
all expectations. Nevertheless, micro-biologists continued to discover
a whole series of new antibiotics which, while demonstrating the
general character of the phenomenon observed by Fleming, were
apparently so unstable, and subject to so much contamination
by many impurities, that all clinical application seemed ruled out.
However, a demonstration by the French micro-biologist, René
Dubos, working in the laboratories of the Rockefeller Foundation
in New York, of the possibility of experimental modifications and
of directing the antagonism of micro-organisms against other
bacteria, was soon to lead to considerable improvements in the
conditions that had previously been so unfavourable to chemical
research. If the immediate hopes aroused by Dubos' discovery
of a new antibiotic that seemed capable of clinical application, viz.
tyrothricin, were partially ruined by the discovery that the substance was haemolytic, at least Dubos' work led to a result that
Fleming had failed to obtain: it drew the attention of many research
workers to the significance and importance of various problems
linked with the phenomenon of antibiosis.

It was in this climate of very keen interest, so eminently

favourable to scientific research, that two scientists with a very different background, the German chemist E. B. Chain, who was a refugee in England, and H. W. Florey, a pathologist of Australian origin, decided to combine their efforts and knowledge in pursuing with far greater resources the work begun by Fleming. Aware of the difficulty of the problems they had to solve, they managed to gather around them a group of competent biochemists, biologists, pathologists and clinicians, the famous 'Oxford Team'. Where a single scientist with only a very modest laboratory had failed, the far greater resources and the co-operation of scientists, trained in different techniques and methods of research, enabled these investigators to triumph over the principal difficulties of large-scale experiments on the anti-bacterial properties of penicillin.

The first important obstacle was the instability of the final substance, which impeded all practical applications. After many long attempts the Oxford chemists finally managed to prepare a product that was relatively stable and contained sodium penicillate as its active principle.

The anti-bacterial power of the substance obtained was so astonishing that the research workers first thought that they had isolated the active principle of the substance secreted by *penicillium* in an almost pure state. At the time this seemed to be confirmed by the pharmacological study of the properties; and Florey immediately made the first experiments *in vivo* to investigate whether the product conserved its anti-bacterial properties in living organisms. Mice were infected with staphylococci, and while some were treated with the preparation, others were left without treatment. On the next day the research workers, with understandable emotion, discovered that all the untreated mice had died, while those which had been subjected to the action of penicillin were still alive. As Desiderio Papp, from whose beautiful study on the history of the story of penicillin[1] we have borrowed liberally, justly remarked, this experiment, both in the circumstances under which it was made and also in the far-reaching extent of its consequences, is comparable with Pasteur's experiment of vaccinating sheep against anthrax at Pouilly le Fort. Thus these two rigorous investigations,

[1] *Rev. Hist. Sc.*, Vol. VII, 1954. (*See also* B. Sokoloff, *The Story of Penicillin*, Chicago, 1954.)

PLATE XIII

ARCHIMEDES erster erfinder scharpffsinniger vergleichung/
Wag vnd Gewicht/durch außfluß des Wassers.

A SIXTEENTH-CENTURY ETCHING ILLUSTRATING PLUTARCH'S
ACCOUNT OF ARCHIMEDES' DISCOVERY OF THE LAW ON THE
UPTHRUST OF LIQUIDS

*Near Archimedes' bathtub can be seen Hieron's famous crown, and
also various other objects used in hydrostatics (spheres of different
diameter, tanks with taps at different levels, etc.).*

*(Der furnembsten notwendigsten der gantzen Architektur angehörigen
mathematischen und mechanischen Kunst. . . . W. H. Ryff, Nuremburg,
1547).*

PLATE XIV

ONE OF THE PLATES FROM GALVANI'S WORK ON ANIMAL ELECTRICITY

De viribus electricitatis, Utinae, 1792, pl. II

The different pictures illustrate some of Galvani's explanations of the effects of discharges from electric condensers (Leyden Jars) on the nerves of frogs and other animals. Although Galvani failed to interpret the phenomenon correctly, his work enabled Volta to make the major discovery of the electric cell.

PLATE XV

DETAIL OF A PAINTING BY GIUSEPPE BERTINI OF VOLTA'S PRESENTATION TO
NAPOLEON OF HIS FIRST ELECTRIC CELL

*This painting, made many years after the event, recalls the keen interest which
Napoleon showed in an invention which became increasingly important during the
nineteenth century.*

PLATE XVI

Soft iron ring used by Faraday in his discovery of electromagnetic induction on 29th August, 1831 (cf. Fig. 6)

One of the two wires surrounding the core is connected to a battery, the other to a simple galvanometer consisting of a copper wire running over a magnetized needle. On making the primary circuit, the needle is sharply deflected to return to its original position after some oscillations. The needle is also deflected when the circuit is broken. The deflections are due to the fact that a current is induced in the secondary winding whenever there is a change of current in the primary circuit. Despite its primitive nature, this apparatus led to a discovery whose importance can hardly be over-estimated.

whose original failure had been so discouraging in both cases, were eventually to fulfil such high hopes.

The therapeutic value of penicillin having been demonstrated, there only remained the study of, and the extension of experiment to, various bacterial infections in which it had shown its action *in vitro*, and finally, after having applied it to human beings with all the necessary precautions and indispensable strictness of method, to prepare it on an industrial scale which alone could lead to its general use. Although the success of Florey's first experiment had solved most of the theoretical problems that he had inherited from Fleming, the new obstacles which had to be surmounted in passing from laboratory experiments to industrial processes were also very delicate, if of a different nature. In less troubled times this new phase in the history of penicillin would probably have been tackled on a relatively modest scale, at least at the outset, since pharmaceutical firms would not have taken the initiative of investing a large capital until such time as definite success was assured. But Florey's first conclusive attempts were made in August 1941, during the Second World War, at a moment when the solution of the problems arising out of the industrial manufacture of penicillin and the general use of its anti-bacterial effects, were of extreme urgency and importance. Thus the study of the many problems involved was considered by Great Britain and by the United States as an essential aspect of the immense war effort in the scientific field, and it was undertaken on a tremendous scale. Two of the chief engineers of the success of the Oxford team, Florey and Heatley, went to the United States and directed the work of many hundreds of research workers and technicians, having at their disposal the considerable material resources of the public services and the largest pharmaceutical companies. The systematic attack on the problems of the industrial manufacture of penicillin, and that of its therapeutic applications, was thus truly under way, and, in 1943, brilliant results were to reward the efforts of various groups of research workers (Plate XVIIIB).

Without further insistence on either this phase or on the subsequent stages of the practical application of various antibiotics, it seems particularly worth-while to see what we can learn from the circumstances themselves under which research work managed to endow medicine with so powerful a new weapon. Ignoring the problem of the precursors, which will be treated in another chapter, we shall try first of all to assess the play of chance in this more or less systematic sequence of discoveries, observations and experiments.

The contamination of Fleming's culture of staphylococci is for most laymen a typical example of those many manifestations of chance which are at the origin of many of the most striking discoveries. But as we have noted already, even if the contamination of microbe preparations in a badly equipped laboratory, lacking the indispensable conditions for asepsis, is a fortunate accident, it is nevertheless common enough not to attract the attention of all observers. If, in fact, chance did play a part, it was in the concurrence of two extremely favourable circumstances, on the one hand the fact that of all the many varieties of airborne micro-organisms capable of contaminating the preparation, it had to be just the fungus-producing penicillin, found only in small quantities in the air, which infected the plate, and on the other hand that there happened to be a culture of staphylococci which are particularly sensitive to the antibiotic action of penicillin. But if in this initial incident there was an intervention of particularly favourable circumstances, demonstrating the antibiotic action of certain micro-organisms, we must agree with D. Papp that this 'chance' occurred to a research worker who was ready to appreciate the immense significance of the phenomenon. In fact, Fleming had been trying for some years to prepare an ideal antiseptic having maximum bactericidal properties together with minimum toxicity to the human organism. Thus, however fortuitous the phenomena, he could not but have taken a direct interest in them. Furthermore, it is almost certain that the phenomenon of antibiosis must have appeared on other occasions without being noticed by observers less inclined to appreciate its full importance. The best proof of this is that it was discovered on at least three occasions by particularly well-qualified workers: in 1875 by the English biologist Tyndall, in the course of studies directed towards refuting the theory of spontaneous generation; in 1877 by Pasteur and his collaborator, the physicist Jules Joubert;[1] and finally by Fleming in 1928. It would seem that there is no better example to validate

[1] See p. 113.

Pasteur's opinion, that in research chance only helps those whose minds are well prepared for it.

Despite the preponderant part played by the individual qualities of the research workers, circumstances can equally favour certain stages of the development of discoveries. The second stage of the history of penicillin will give us a fresh example of this. We have seen that the Oxford team had managed to prepare a very stable solid extract which they thought was identical with the active principle of the secretion of *penicillium* in its almost pure state. In fact this product, as was established later, was only a heterogeneous mixture containing 99 per cent of impurities and only 1 per cent of penicillin. If the total effect of these impurities had been toxic, this fact would have masked the non-toxicity of penicillin and would have prevented the investigators from recognizing its beneficial therapeutic effects. Very fortunately this was not the case, and this first favourable factor was coupled with another, also very important. Florey was fortunate in that instead of experimenting with guinea-pigs, he used mice. Had he used the former, which are so common in laboratories, he would have obtained a negative and discouraging result, since penicillin is a very violent poison in their case. Thus favourable circumstances have at least contributed to the successes in the two first phases of the history of penicillin. Nevertheless, we must not draw too hasty a conclusion from it. Had they been less favourable, these factors could not have prevented the discovery of antibiotics. They would only have retarded it for some years. In fact, if we compare the relative lack of success of the attempts on the part of Fleming's precursors during the last part of the nineteenth century with the magnificent success that crowned the efforts of the real discoverers of penicillin, we are led to seek the chief causes of the immense advances made during the twentieth century in the fields of micro-biology and chemistry in the collective work of teams of specialists of various schools, and in the far greater and more perfect technical resources. Thus without wishing to minimize in this discovery either the essential role of the brilliant qualities of such scientists as Fleming, Florey, Chain or Dubos, or the more or less fortuitous role of some fortunate factors, it seems fair to consider that the discovery of antibiotics is essentially a victory of the science and the techniques of the twentieth century.

CHAPTER VIII

THE ROLE OF ERROR

SIMPLIFYING ERRORS. THE EXAMPLE OF KEPLER

It is certain that in the very large majority of cases errors of observation, of calculation or of interpretation are harmful to scientific research. Mistaken conclusions can often be put right only after long and unproductive verifications. Furthermore, there are some errors which, having been misunderstood for a long time, impair or retard the development of very large fields of science. Nevertheless there are other errors which, by the incentives or simplifications that they contain, have played an essential role in the discovery of facts or of fundamental principles. This fact may well appear paradoxical on first examination, but if we realize that the apparent simplicity of numerous physical phenomena is nothing but a first approximation of a very much more complex reality, we shall understand that many laws could only have been discovered by means of over-simplified hypotheses and of observations, in which grossly approximate measurements minimized certain difficulties that otherwise might have prevented progress in thought. A first particularly characteristic example is Kepler's statement of the three laws governing the motion of the planets of the solar system. This will give us a very good idea of the many ways in which erroneous theories or even material errors of many kinds can play a favourable role in the discovery of fundamental laws, and the example will also lead to some general considerations. Thus we shall devote quite some space to it, particularly since it is an example that deals with the foundations of celestial mechanics, and which, furthermore, has some of the essential characteristics of the many more modern examples we have chosen.

Born in Weil, in Würtemberg, on the 27th December, 1571, Johann Kepler studied at the University of Tübingen, where the astronomer Michael Mästlin determined Kepler's vocation by introducing him to the heliocentric system of Copernicus. In 1596, at the age of twenty-six years, he published his first work, the *Mysterium Cosmographicum*,[1] in which he produced new arguments in favour of the Copernican theory, and where he showed that the planes of the planetary orbits are close to one another but distinct. Copernicus was wrong in thinking that these different planes pass through the centre of the terrestrial orbit—an error which had disturbed and partially impaired his research work— and Kepler established that in reality their common point is the Sun.

But this work shows, in the case of its author also, conceptions which might strike us as very strange. In fact Kepler thought that the planetary system was organized according to the five regular polyhedra known from the time of the ancient geometers (*see* Plate XIX). This mystical conception, to which Kepler always remained faithful, was taken from the Platonic theories on the affinity between geometrical figures and the perceptible properties of the elements which they are supposed to represent. For Kepler this was more than a mere intellectual diversion. Kepler, like many scientists of his time, was filled with mystical ideas, and in order to relate the motion of the stars in the solar system to regular polyhedra and to musical harmonics, he attempted an accurate determination of the geometry and kinematics of the trajectories of the stars. True, such a mystic approach in itself could not suffice for creating so important a work as his, and very fortunately Kepler had, along with his mysticism, all the apparently incompatible qualities and resources of the authentic scientist. In fact it was observation and concrete fact which he considered as the basis to which he must adjust all his hypotheses, abandoning those that would not fit and modifying those he thought capable of improvement. It was thus that he directed his patient and exemplarily painstaking calculations towards trying to verify the validity of the ideas that sprang from his creative imagination. This was to lead him to his main discovery and gave him the courage to persevere in the face of the many difficulties that he was to meet during a life often marked by painful and dramatic incidents.

It is understandable that such a man might look somewhat irrational to the eyes of the modern scientist. To appreciate him

[1] The full title of his work was *Prodromus Dissertationum Cosmographicorum continens mysterium Cosmographicum de admirabili Proportione Orbium Cælestium, deque causis Cælorum numeri, magnitudinis, motuumque periodicorum genuinis et propriis, demonstratum per quinque regularia corpora Geometrica.*

we must enter into the spirit of the beginning of the seventeenth century when wars and pillage, witch-hunts and religious strife were the background to a scientific life. Here a love for tradition and for the hard work that preceded the creation of new scientific concepts was tempered by an infatuation with ancient myths, scholastic discussions, and the speculations of astrologers, alchemists and the disciples of Paracelsus.

We are, in fact, in a period in which the first mutterings of the experimental method and the progress of observational science revealed, in the concrete structure of the universe and of nature, a variety and an order that had previously been beyond even the imagination. Thus it was natural that attempts were made to explain these marvels by new and audacious theories. If today we can easily distinguish between rational and mystical conceptions in these theories, such a distinction was very much more difficult for scientists at the beginning of the seventeenth century, whose entire education had conditioned them to seeing a constant intervention of the supernatural in the development of physical phenomena.

That fundamental errors were the basis of a great deal of progress during this time is a fact which can be seen in all branches of science, ranging from astronomy to chemistry, physics, anatomy and medicine. The realms to be tackled were so vast that, however erroneous the starting-point, the working hypotheses and the interpretations, any systematic research work had to lead to an increase in knowledge.

Within this framework, however, Kepler's situation is a very particular one. His emphasis on mysticism was a little unusual even in his period, but nevertheless the laws which he discovered are typical examples of strict modern scientific laws.

In a rapid sketch of the genesis of his famous laws on the motion of the planets of the Solar system we shall try to show how some misconceptions were able to play a favourable role, while others stood in the way of the progressive development of ideas. We shall also find that, for Kepler, it was observation alone that decided the validity of the scientific laws, and that it is to this conception, which is the basis of modern science, that the success of his research work is due.

In his *Mysterium Cosmographicum* of 1597, Kepler had already directed his attention to the study of the structure of the Solar system. However, in order to continue his research work he had to start from more precise astronomical observations than those which were then at his disposal. Circumstances were soon to provide these indispensable data in bringing to his knowledge the considerable number of observations of the best observer of the times, the Danish astronomer Tycho Brahe (1546–1601). In fact when, in the course of the year 1600, the publication of an edict against Protestants obliged Kepler to quit the Chair which he had occupied in Gratz since 1594, Tycho Brahe, who was then mathematician to the Emperor Rudolph II at Prague, invited him to come to work with him. The Danish astronomer was then trying to perfect a new theory of the planet Mars, and Kepler assisted him actively in his research work. Tycho Brahe died in the following year and Kepler succeeded him as court mathematician. Tycho's heirs left him the manuscripts and the observational notes of the great observer. Kepler profited from these, and began a new and highly individual study of the theory of Mars, and after long efforts his research work led to his three famous laws which are one of the pillars of modern astronomy.

In 1604 and 1605 he had discovered the two first laws of the planetary system, viz. the law of areas which gives an accurate kinematic determination of the motion of every planet by stating that the area traversed by the radius vector joining it to the Sun is proportional to the time; and the geometric law stating that the orbits of the planets are ellipses with one focus at the Sun. These laws put an end to the thousand-year-old belief, which had still been held by Copernicus, in the absolute pre-eminence of circular motion.

This double discovery, which Kepler announced in 1609 in his *Astronomia Nova*, published under the auspices of Emperor Rudolph, was the result of a long series of hypotheses, arguments and calculations.

To determine the displacement of a planet such as Mars, the astronomer had to overcome considerable obstacles resulting from the simultaneous displacement of his point of observation. In the first stage of his work Kepler had tried to gain a better knowledge of the orbit of the earth. To do so he needed a fixed reference system, for which purpose he chose intervals of 687 days, which Tycho Brahe had shown to be the duration of a full revolution of Mars. Thus having a fixed line of reference, viz. the line joining the

Sun to that point of the orbit of Mars to which the planet returns after each revolution, Kepler could fix different points of the earth's orbit. His first calculations showed him that these points could be represented by a circle whose centre is at a distance from the Sun equal to 18/1000 of its radius. During the first phases of his researches this seemed to confirm, at least as a working hypothesis, Ptolemy's theory of eccentricities, and enabled him to improve the corresponding data for the earth's orbit. The small eccentricity of this orbit favoured Kepler's calculations and justified, at least as a first approximation, this false but simplifying hypothesis.

Knowing accurately the orbit of the earth, Kepler could then begin the kinematic study of the motion of Mars. His starting hypothesis was entirely erroneous; he thought that a force similar to a magnetic one produced by the rotation of the Sun about its own axis was the cause of the motion of the planets. He thought that for each planet P, this force produced in the Sun S, acts tangentially to the orbit of P; its intensity being inversely proportional to its distance from S, viz. $S\,P = r$. He believed he could thus deduce that the velocity of a planet is always proportional to $1/r$. Newton's discovery of the law of universal gravitation has shown that this conception was inexact, but that the error which it introduced was cancelled out at the two extremities of the axis of the orbit; since Kepler's investigations were restricted to these points alone, he could not have detected his error.

From this theory it would appear that the time taken by a planet to traverse an elementary arc $P\,P' = d\,s$ of its orbit, is proportional both to $S\,P$ and to $d\,s$. By dividing a finite arc in this series of elementary arcs of equal length, it can be shown that the time taken to traverse this arc is proportional to the sum of the vector radii of the different points of division. To develop this argument, integration would have been essential, and since Kepler was unable to tackle it, he replaced the sum of the radii by the area of the sector traversed by the planet. This was a grave error of principle, and Kepler was fully aware of it. However, since the error allowed him to deduce his law of areas, which he knew to conform to the observations at his disposal, he retained it short of a better explanation.

These two successive errors, one involuntary, the other conscious, led him to a physical law whose accuracy he verified. While

PLATE XVII

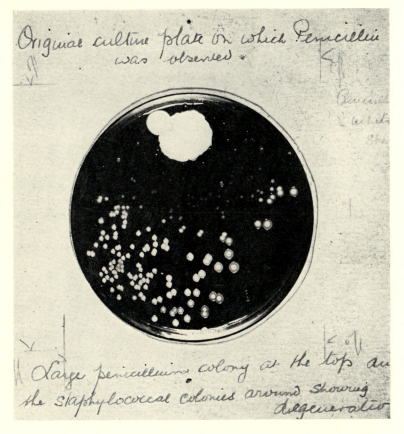

THE ORIGINAL PLATE CONTAINING THE CULTURE IN WHICH SIR ALEXANDER
FLEMING DISCOVERED THE ANTI-BIOTIC ACTION OF PENICILLIN

A large colony of Penicillium *can be seen in the upper part of the preparation.
The surrounding colonies of staphylococci show obvious signs of degeneration.*

PLATE XVIII

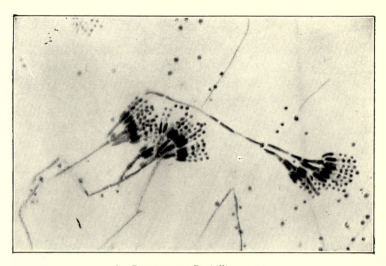

A. Culture of *Penicillium notatum*
(Czapek-Dox medium; magnification × 500)
Note the hyphae of the mycelium with conidiophores, conidia and free spores.

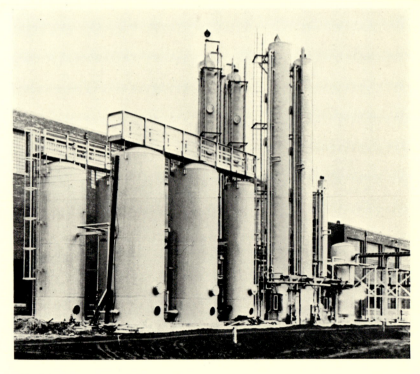

B. Section of one of the first large factories for the manufacture of
penicillin in the United States

he regretted the inadequacy, or at least the error of his hypothesis, the agreement with facts led Kepler to consider the second phase of his work as certain enough for him to proceed to further work.

Having now an accurate enough terrestrial orbit and a correct kinematic law, Kepler tried to determine the orbit of Mars. Based on two observations made at an interval of 687 days (the duration of one revolution of Mars), one particular position of Mars and the two corresponding positions of the earth could be determined by the law of areas, and a simple process of triangulation would then give the distance of Mars. In repeating this operation a sufficient number of times, different points are obtained which should have given an adequate idea of the trajectory of this planet.

When, after long calculations, Kepler had obtained this result, he tried to interpret it. Starting first of all from the theory of epicycles, he determined the assumed circles by means of points in the neighbourhood of the apsides.[1] But when he compared the other positions observed by Tycho Brahe with those obtained by this theory, Kepler discovered an error of eight minutes in some of these.[2]

With great acumen he saw that the cause of this error was not to be sought in the imperfections of Tycho's observations but in the erroneous character of his starting hypothesis.

'Divine Mercy,' he wrote later on, with the calm assurance which comes once success is assured, 'has given us in Tycho an observer so faithful that he could not possibly have made this error of eight minutes. We must thank God and take advantage of this situation; we must discover where our assumptions have gone wrong. . . . These eight minutes, which we dare not neglect, will give us a means of reforming the whole of astronomy.'

In trying to create a new theory that would agree better with the observational data, Kepler noticed that all the discrepant points lay inside the circle that he had constructed. He then tried to replace the circle by an oval whose point was at the perihelium, the point of the orbit nearest to the Sun; but the application of the law of areas to such a trajectory proved to be particularly difficult, and also led to imperfect agreement with the observations. Finally,

[1] The extremities of the major axes of the planetary orbit.
[2] This error is due to the fact that the eccentricity of the orbit of Mars (0·093) is relatively important, while in Kepler's somewhat inaccurate observations that of the terrestrial orbit still agreed with the circular hypothesis.

G

after new fruitless attempts, complicated at one time by an error of calculation, he discovered that the hypothesis of an ellipse, of which the sun is one of the foci, agreed perfectly with the observational data and led to an easy application of the law of areas (*see* Plate XX). Then his enthusiasm knew no bounds. 'I awoke,' he wrote, 'from a deep sleep and a new light fell upon me.' And, in the dedication to the Emperor Rudolph II in his *Astronomia Nova*, he speaks of this achievement in allegorical terms, unfamiliar to the modern reader:

'I am presenting your Majesty with a noble prisoner, the fruit of a laborious and difficult war waged under your auspices. . . . No other human invention has ever triumphed more completely; in vain had all astronomers prepared for the struggle, in vain had they put their resources to work, their troops into the fields. Mars, laughing at their endeavours, had destroyed their machines and ruined their hopes; quietly, he had entrenched himself in the impenetrable secret of his empire and had camouflaged his cunning path from the enemy's search. . . . As for me, I must above all praise the work and the devotion of the valiant captain Tycho Brahe. . . . His observations, which have guided me, have helped me to banish this vague and undefined fear which one experiences when first confronted with an unknown foe. . . . During the uncertainties of the struggle, what disasters, what scourges have not devastated our camp. The loss of an illustrious captain, mutiny of the troops, contagious diseases, all added to our distress. Domestic fortunes and misfortunes robbed me of precious time. Soldiers, deprived of everything, deserted *en masse*; the new recruits were ignorant of the manœuvres, and to add to our misery, provisions were lacking.

'Finally, the enemy resigned himself to peace, and by the intervention of his mother, Nature, he sent me note of his defeat, became a prisoner on parole, and Arithmetic and Geometry escorted him unresisting into our camp.'

After having declared his intention of tackling the study of the trajectories of other planets, Kepler finished with a pressing demand for money.

In fact, his task was far from ended. If the application of the two laws he had discovered was relatively easy for determining the trajectories of other planets, to complete his work he had still to discover the relations holding between the motions of all the planets themselves. True, in his *Mysterium Cosmographicum* he had already tackled this problem, but his attempted solution was based on mysticism rather than on accurate observations.

'Take the sphere of the earth as a first measure,' he wrote, 'and circumscribe a regular dodecahedron; then the sphere which contains this is that of Mars. Circumscribe a regular tetrahedron and the sphere which contains it will be that of Jupiter. Again circumscribe a cube and the sphere which encloses it will be that of Saturn. On the other hand, in the sphere of the earth inscribe an isocahedron and the sphere inscribed in this will be that of Venus. Finally, in the latter, inscribe an octahedron and the sphere inscribed will be that of Mercury.'

Kepler returned to the same problem when he prepared his *Harmonices mundi*, the voluminous work published in 1619, which contains an odd assortment of detailed calculations and long mystical arguments. It was only on the 8th March, 1618, that he caught a glimpse of the law which relates the duration of revolution to the dimensions of the axis of the orbit of different planets, but, misled by an error of calculation, he was delayed for some time before returning to it definitely on the 15th May. As was his custom, it was with unrestricted enthusiasm that he announced this discovery in the last book of his work, embedded in a jumble of discourses whose mystical inspiration and whose lack of coherence contrasted most strikingly with his 'austere grandeur'.

'The proportion between the mean distances of two planets is in exact sesquialter proportion to the periodic times,' which we formulate as 'The square of the period of one revolution is proportional to the cube of the major axis of the orbit.'

Thus the system of Ptolemy, and the ancient conceptions of the architecture of the Solar system, were definitely eliminated by the three kinematic laws which completed and confirmed the heliocentric theory of Copernicus. It is almost incredible that so rigorously constructed an edifice could have been conceived and demonstrated by a man whose mystical conceptions were so far removed from those to which the triumph of modern science was to lead some years later on. However, our examination of the conditions under which these discoveries were made has shown us that in reality an already modern scientific method was hidden under this apparent mysticism. Furthermore, a brief survey of the circumstances will suggest other significant reflections.

It is first of all essential to note that just as the circles of Ptolemy only agreed with the planetary orbits as a first approximation, so Kepler's ellipses did not describe them accurately, but gave a second approximation. In fact they correspond to a purely theoretical case only, viz. the displacement of a planet P under the attraction of the Sun alone. Now the other planets also, if to a smaller degree, affect the motion of P, and the perturbations which they cause in the motion of this planet produce deviations from the beautiful simplicity of Kepler's laws.

It was the admirable intuition of the great astronomer, and the increasing precision introduced by Tycho Brahe into astronomical observation, that were the essential elements permitting the construction of this magnificent edifice which was to allow Newton, three-quarters of a century later, to evolve his theory of universal gravitation. Thus a marked progress in observational techniques led to a consolidation of essential theory. However, the question might legitimately be asked whether Kepler would have been able to arrive at his famous laws had he had observations more accurate than those of Tycho Brahe, which, it is essential to note, were made with the naked eye. Now, at the time of Tycho's death in 1601, the telescope was already in existence—at least potentially so—but nobody had yet dreamt of using this instrument for astronomical observations. This is what Galileo did for the first time in 1610. Had so versatile an observer as Tycho Brahe had access to this instrument, he would certainly not have hesitated—as Picard did as late as 1668—to adapt the existing measuring instruments, thus obtaining much more precise results. This might well have caused Kepler's schematizations to be hidden by the complexity of the data.

This shows, in a particularly striking way, that most theories of physical phenomena evolve by means of successive approximations only, and that in every epoch the precision of theories is very closely linked with the means of observation. Every advance in methods of observation or in measuring procedures leads, within a relatively short period of time, to a revision of the corresponding theories, and sooner or later to the creation of new theories that are in closer correspondence with reality. Whenever this correspondence

is lacking, the efforts of theoreticians become bent on removing all
obstacles in its path. Thus every successive stage in the evolution
of experimental and of observational science is associated with
the evolution of theory, comparable both in level and in complexity.
Too rapid an advance of one of the fields leads to far greater
difficulties of adaptation in the other.

Returning to the particular problem of the elaboration of
Kepler's laws, we shall find that other elements also played a role
of equal importance, owing to which many over-simplifications
were introduced most effectively. We have already noticed the
fact that since the mass of the Sun is far greater than that of the
other planets, the gravitational pull of the latter is of a very much
smaller order of magnitude than that of the Sun, and may thus
be considered as negligible in a first approximation. On the other
hand the small eccentricity of the earth's orbit makes it possible
for the circle that Kepler used as his starting-point to give a good
approximation of the successive positions of the earth, while,
because of the much greater order of magnitude of the eccentricity
of the orbit of Mars, the elliptical character of this trajectory can
be demonstrated even more easily.

We may judge from these necessarily somewhat summary
explanations how many different obstacles Kepler had to overcome,
and how very surprising had been the role played by the intervention of favourable and unfavourable errors, and also by more or
less solidly elaborated over-simplifications and by mystical specula-
tion without any rational foundation. It is from this convergence
of different and apparently contradictory elements that there has
arisen one of the essential advances in astronomy. All the greater
must be our tribute to Kepler, to his audacious and brilliant intuitions, his powers of observation, his obstinate perseverance and
his desire to base astronomy on solid and rational foundations.

THE FRUITFULNESS OF CERTAIN ERRORS

Over and above its favourable influence on the discovery of
theories whose simplicity results from the fact that they are only
first approximations of a much more complex reality, error has
played a paradoxically fruitful role in some discoveries.

A very typical example is the discovery of natural radioactivity, which we have discussed in another chapter.[1] It was an inaccurate hypothesis of Henri Poincaré on the role played by the fluorescent side of the Crookes's tube in the production of X-rays which was the basis of the experiments that were to lead Henri Becquerel to the discovery of the radioactivity of uranium compounds.

This fact is by no means exceptional, and we should meet many further examples of it, were all inventors to give a complete description of the circumstances of the genesis of their chief discovery. In fact any starting hypothesis may be fruitful if it leads to original calculations or new experiments, provided only that it is considered simply as a hypothesis to be verified and controlled, and not as being of overriding importance, thus deflecting research workers from the necessary objectivity.[2]

Even in mathematics such examples of fruitful errors are not rare, and Henri Lebesgue shows how the verification of one of his theorems, while revealing an error of reasoning, also provided a natural path towards a great extension of the field of analysis.

'The consideration of discontinuous functions had so enlarged the field of analysis, that one might have felt some little disquiet. Nevertheless, one still had the hope that of all the functions and of all the aggregates conceived, Baire's functions and the measurable aggregates associated with them, occurred exclusively in mathematics; since it appeared that all operations on these functions and aggregates would always lead to functions and aggregates of the same families. This analysis seemed to have an inherent principle of limitation.

'To determine if this was actually the case, it was necessary to make a special examination of the solution of equations leading to implicit functions. In the course of this study I formulated the following: The projection of a measurable aggregate B is always a measurable aggregate B. The demonstration was simple and short, but wrong. M. Lusin, at that time a young lecturer, and M. Sousbin, one of his first pupils, noticed the mistake and tried to correct it. I think that at the start they believed this would be an easy matter, but the difficulties emerged quickly and they began to doubt the formulation itself, and then disproved it by submitting it to a test.

---

[1] See pp. 62 ff: *From Cathode Rays to Radium*.
[2] This is the sound advice given by Claude Bernard in his *Introduction à l'étude de la médécine expérimentale*.

'Thus the analysis has no inherent principle of limitation. If the family of Baire functions is vast enough to make one giddy, the field of analysis is vaster still. And how much vaster!'[1]

Another example of fruitful error is Fermat's conjecture that all integers of the form $2^{2^n} + 1$ are primes. In reality, this hypothesis was wrong, as Euler was able to demonstrate, but it was nevertheless the basis of a great deal of important work in arithmetic.

A still better-known example is that of Fermat's famous assertion that it is impossible to factorize into integers the equation $x^n + y^n = z^n$ for values of n higher than 2. This problem evidently differs from the preceding examples, for neither its general correctness nor its erroneous character have so far been demonstrated. Despite this fact, this problem has led to very fruitful results, which may be shown by means of a simple example. In 1845 the German mathematician Kummer believed that he had solved the famous problem, but his demonstration contained an error that was pointed out to him by Lejeune Dirichlet. This error rested on an assumption which Kummer had wrongly considered as self-evident, and which he then hastened to study more closely. His deeper studies in this direction led him to a discovery with immense consequences, that of ideals which in turn were to lead him to the theory of algebraic numbers, one of the keys to the road of modern algebra.

FALSE PROBLEMS

To complete this rapid survey of the various forms under which error can play a part in scientific discovery, we must recall the fact that some impossible problems and some false manipulations have at different times led to numerous results from which science was later to profit.

Since we cannot here undertake a detailed study of this intervention of extra-scientific ideas on the development of science, we shall merely mention some of the most striking examples.

Attempts to square the circle have in effect been the root of much work, some of which has led to very important new results; in physics many of the advances in mechanics are due to endeavours

---

[1] H. Lebesgue, preface to the *Leçons sur les ensembles analytiques et leur applications*, by N. Lusin, Paris, Gauthier-Villars, 1930.

to produce perpetual motion; many of the original astronomical discoveries arose out of astrological preoccupations, and the advance in this branch of science would certainly have been slower if the material means at the disposal of astrologers could not have served equally well for precise astronomical measurements. The same is the case in chemistry, where the work of alchemists and of the disciples of Paracelsus supplied the scientists of the seventeenth and eighteenth centuries with a rich harvest of experimental facts.

DISCREPANCIES BETWEEN THEORY AND EXPERIMENT

We must finally recall the particularly fruitful role played in many scientific discoveries by discrepancies between theoretical predictions and real facts. Without underestimating the influence of other factors, it is not an exaggeration to claim that most experimental discoveries are due to such discrepancies. We shall cite two striking examples only. The discrepancy between the actual speed of propagation of sound in air and that predicted by Newton's theory remained for nearly a century a kind of scientific scandal which many scientists tried in vain to explain. This difficulty was resolved by Laplace who, in 1816, showed that this discrepancy was due to the fact that the theory ignored changes in temperature produced by the compression of the air. In drawing the attention of physicists to problems connected with the compression of gases, the solution of this puzzle was to open the way to Mayer's determination of the mechanical equivalent of heat.

In astronomy, the discovery of the discrepancy between the real positions of the planets, and those furnished by too summary an application of Newton's law, gave rise to the theory of perturbations, which is the most fruitful application of a general method, i.e. that of residuals. Astronomers were slowly led to a ceaseless and more accurate study of the motion of various heavenly bodies. The demonstration of variations in the eccentricity of the terrestrial orbit and the discovery of two new planets, Neptune and Pluto, are some of the most brilliant triumphs of this method, whose most recent success is the decisive argument in favour of relativity theory provided by two perturbations, known for a long time but previously unexplained, viz. the acceleration of the perihelium of Mercury and of Mars.

PART THREE

Various Aspects of Discoveries

CHAPTER IX

THE ORIGINALITY OF DISCOVERIES

WHEN a discovery, attributed to a scientist, becomes well known and takes its rightful place in the body of scientific dogma, it frequently happens that claims of priority are made on behalf of contemporary workers or of relatively distant precursors.

Thus the question of the true authorship of a discovery confronts the historian of science with an extremely difficult and complex problem, often obscured by questions of vanity, of personal rivalries and even of chauvinism. A due regard for objectivity and for scientific integrity in the attentive and critical study of all the publications dealing with this question, and of the reports of academic sessions and of the correspondence between scientists, is the only safe guide to the historian in this difficult research work.

In fact, attentive study of the development of science reveals that there are few major discoveries which have not been prepared by a great deal of preliminary work, often on the part of obscure scientists. To be just to these precursors is one of the historian's tasks, and in fulfilling it he has a good opportunity of assessing the complexity and the continuity of all scientific evolution. However, this task is full of difficulties and dangers. It involves an assessment of the extent to which every precursor had been able to grasp the nature, significance, importance and consequences of a particular discovery, and a study of the subsequent repercussions of his contribution, before the precursor's possible influence on the work of the 'true discoverer' can be judged.

We are thus led to distinguish between true precursors and simple anticipators whose ideas remained either too undefined or else based on inadequate arguments.

We must equally consider those discoveries which, while they were actually made, remained unpublished or fell into complete oblivion. While their authors deserve credit, this does not in the least diminish that of the scientist who had subsequently to rediscover the same facts completely independently.

As regards the question of priorities, many rest on quite illegitimate interpretations made after the event, and on partial results of which the author did not appreciate the importance nor try to pursue the studies. Others, again, rest on more serious arguments and prove that many discoveries for which the ground has been prepared can arise almost simultaneously in the minds of many scientists.

Various examples, taken from different fields of science, will allow us to assess the complexity of the questions raised by the problem of precursors and by discussions of priority. The fact that a considerable number of great discoveries were made almost simultaneously by different scientists, working independently, will show that great discoveries often arise when the general level attained by the science of the times renders them almost inevitable.

THE PROBLEM OF PRECURSORS

(a) Original Studies of Malaria

In his *Biologie de l'Invention*, Charles Nicolle gives an example of a precursor whose ideas, although very interesting, did not in the least influence the effective march of science.[1] This was a very acute observation in the eighteenth century of the role played by mosquitoes in the transmission of malaria, made by a priest who lived in a part of Dalmatia where malaria was widespread. What is particularly relevant is the fact that it was not reported in a scientific paper, but in a description by the Abbé de Fortiz, *Le Voyage en Dalmatie.*

'All the inhabitants of this area [the lower course of the Narenta river] sleep in open porches where they can be on their guard against their neighbours. A clergyman . . . a man of lively spirit, told me he suspected that the fevers plaguing the inhabitants of this country were due to the bite of these insects. It is not impossible that the fever is communicated in this way, at least the conjecture is very ingenious.'

If, as seems probable, the opinion of the Dalmatian priest was due to a clear understanding of the relations between protection against mosquito bites, and the prevention of malaria, then in fact

[1] Nicolle, *op. cit.*

this was the work of an authentic precursor. If not, if it was merely a passing thought, of which there is a surfeit, mostly fruitless or devoid of any significance, then it hardly deserves a mention.

We must note in this connection that the definite rediscovery of the role of mosquitoes in the transmission of malaria was made almost a century later by a means that assured its success and its prompt dissemination. It was in 1880 in Constantinople that Alphonse Laveran (1845–1922), in the course of some brilliant work on protozoa, demonstrated the existence of haematozoa in the blood of people suffering from malaria. Some years later the Italian histologist and anatomist, Camillo Golgi (1844–1925), gave a precise description of the cycle in the evolution of this parasite. The work of Ronald Ross, of G. Battista Grassi, of Patrick Manson, and of many other research workers, slowly led to a clear understanding of the mechanism of malarial transmission through the agency of some species of mosquitoes.[1] Thus there was explained a complex problem which had puzzled doctors for so long, and which could have been solved much earlier, at least in principle, by the systematic investigation of the hypothesis put forward by an obscure Dalmatian priest and mentioned by de Floris. Let us recall, however, that even before knowing the causes of malaria, physicians had a relatively effective remedy, quinine, which, discovered in 1820 by the famous pharmacists Pelletier and Caventou, had proved a very effective clinical agent in the prevention of this disease. The mechanism of this action was only explained by Laveran, who showed the toxic effect of this substance on haematozoa.

(b) Monge and Musical Quality

Another example of a somewhat different nature is the theory of the quality of musical tones. It was known that the German scientist Hermann von Helmholtz (1821–1894) has shown that every musical note of a particular amplitude is associated with a quality, resulting from the superposition on the fundamental note of a series of harmonics, i.e. pure notes whose frequency is a multiple

[1] For a more detailed study, cf. Castiglioni's *Histoire de la Médecine*, Paris, 1931, Payot, and L. J. Warshaw, *Malaria, the Biography of a Killer*, N.Y., 1949.

of that of the fundamental. This theory was confirmed experiment-
ally by the method of resonators, a technique adapted to the theoretical methods of harmonic analysis of periodic functions. The
simple principle which Helmholtz had deduced from concrete
experiments had already been described by the famous eighteenth-
century musician Rameau, and subsequently, in quite a different
way, by the eminent scientist, Gaspard Monge.

In the preface to his *Nouveau Système de musique théorique*, Jean-
Philippe Rameau showed, in 1726, that the sounds corresponding
to the pronunciation of the vowels *o* and *a* produced different
harmonics apart from the fundamental sound. This first attempt at a
vocal analysis was only resumed in the nineteenth century, when
advances in experimental techniques permitted a more accurate
investigation of vocal sounds.

As regards Monge, he published nothing on this question, but
his very accurate ideas on the theory of musical quality are recorded
by a far less important scientist, Suremain-Missery, who, in a treatise
on acoustics published in 1793, wrote the following on the subject
of musical quality:[1]

'. . . But what then is the general cause to which we can attri-
bute it? I believe that this cause is still to be discovered. I know
well that I have heard M. Monge of the *Académie des Sciences*
say, that what determines such quality can be nothing but such
and such an order or number of vibrations or segments of the
string producing sounds of a given quality; but either because I
did not understand this famous geometrician or because, with all
deference, he himself had been mistaken at the time . . .'

The author then tries to refute Monge's thesis by asserting
the impossibility of superimposing on one and the same
string elementary vibrations of different amplitudes. Then he
adds:

'Now if a string does not divide itself of its own accord, for
this would be inconceivable, how then could its quality be determined by the order or number of vibrations of its segments? It
would, however, appear that this is precisely what M. Monge
implies, for he added that if only one could suppress the vibrations

[1] A. Suremain-Missery, *Théorie acoustico-musicale, ou de la doctrine des sons rap-
portée aux principes de leur combinaison*, Paris, 1793. (*See also Rev. Hist. Sc.*, Vol. III.)

of the segments, all sounding strings, no matter of what material, would surely have the same quality.'

It is certain that Monge could have refuted these objections very easily, because for him the problem was extremely simple. In fact during the years 1771–1772 he had been interested in the theoretical problem of vibrating strings, a question which had excited the passionate interest of mathematicians since the beginnings of the eighteenth century and which had greatly contributed to the creation of the theory of partial differential equations. The initial difficulties once surmounted, this theory permitted the exact explanation of the motion of a vibrating string, and in particular the prediction of the existence of harmonics superimposed on the fundamental note. For a scientist who, like Monge, loved to give concrete interpretations of the theoretical results he had obtained, it was thus very easy to understand the exact nature of musical quality. Highly appreciated as he was both by physicists and by mathematicians, Monge's theory would certainly have been adopted by them. All that was needed was for him to publish it, since the mention which is made of it in the work of Suremain-Missery was obviously no substitute, in view of its small influence and of the polemical way in which Monge's theory was presented in it.

The lack of connection between the mathematics and the experimental physics of that time explains why an idea, familiar to all those mathematicians acquainted with the theory of partial differential equations, was to be so long ignored by physicists. Furthermore, it is this lack of connection between different branches of science and between investigators of different specialities which, at least partially, is the cause of many similar delays in the advance in ideas.

(c) The 'Prehistory' of Antibiotics

One of the reasons why the problem of precursors has such an important place in the history of science is that actually there is no single discovery in which at least partial claims for priority could not be staked. It is, however, essential to note that the evidence of the work of these 'precursors' is generally not produced till

after the event. An example of a recent discovery, that of antibiotics, will tell us how, once a discovery is widely known, the work
of many previously forgotten investigators can assume quite a
new shape and significance, and will also give us a better understanding of the reason why these more or less distant precursors
had to fail, or at least partially so.

In a preceding chapter we have told of the different stages in
the discovery of penicillin, which constituted the first truly scientific
study of antibiotics, applied to the treatment of many bacterial
infections. It is certain that at the time when Fleming first observed
the phenomenon of the antagonism between micro-organisms,
he was unaware that this effect had already been noticed a long
time ago, and had even been applied empirically. Today, when
various aspects of the mechanism of antibiosis have been the object
of careful study, some old observations whose objective value had
previously not been sufficiently appreciated seem to rest on much
better foundations.

Thus, some indications of the physician and botanist Dios-
coridus or of his contemporary in the first century, the famous
Roman encyclopaedist Pliny the Elder (23–79), now appear in
their true light. We must grant that some ancient remedies which,
only twenty years ago, were considered as devoid of all curative
value, could sometimes have had beneficial effects, due to their
antibiotic properties. True, there were no empirical observations
whatsoever prior to Fleming's discovery, the active principle of
the product used being far too mixed with impurities to be truly
effective. However, some of these apparently incongruous in-
gredients used by pre-scientific pharmacists now appear definitely
less fantastic than they had been thought to be.[1]

However, here we are dealing with empirical precursors, who,
without being able to appreciate the nature of the scientific facts,
simply tried, by interpreting traditional observations, to use some of
their consequences. In the nineteenth century, the birth of bac-
teriology and the spreading of Darwin's theory of the struggle for
existence changed the total climate profoundly, and created

[1] Castiglioni notes that when Himly investigated the action of henbane and
belladonna on the pupil in 1800, he had been influenced by the prior reading of
Pliny's account that before operations for cataract the juice of *Anagallis* was introduced into the eye. (*Histoire de la Médecine*, Paris, Payot, 1931.)

PLATE XIX

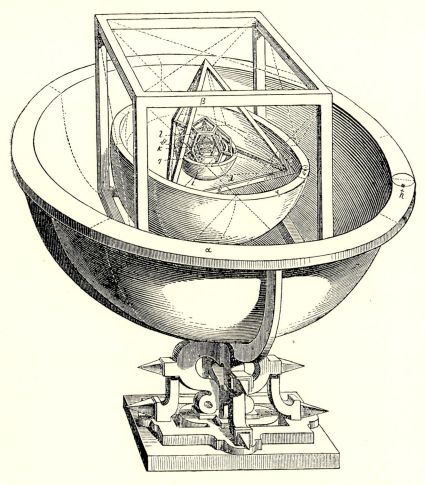

Plate from Kepler's *Mysterium Cosmographicum* (Tubingen 1596) ILLUSTRATING
THE AUTHOR'S CONCEPTION OF THE RELATIONSHIP BETWEEN THE FIVE REGULAR
POLYHEDRA AND THE ORBITS OF THOSE PLANETS THAT WERE KNOWN AT THE TIME

This plate—taken from the first edition of Kepler's Opera Omnia, *vol. I (Frankfort
1858)—shows the influence of mystical and Platonic ideas in Kepler's work on the planetary
orbits.*

*α, Sphere of Saturn. β, Cube. γ, Sphere of Jupiter. δ, Tetrahedron. ε, Sphere of
Mars. ζ, Dodecahedron. η, Earth's Orbit. θ, Icosahedron. ι, Sphere of Venus. χ, Octahedron. λ, Sphere of Mercury. μ, Sun, the immobile centre.*

PLATE XX

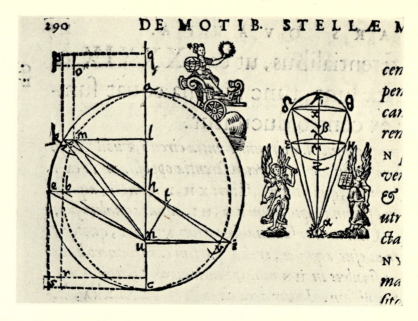

FIGURE FROM KEPLER'S *Astronomia Nova . . .* (*De motibus stellae Martis*, p. 290),
Prague 1609, WHERE HE GIVES HIS PROOF OF THE ELLIPTICITY OF THE TRAJEC-
TORY OF MARS

*The very clear and convincing drawings are surrounded by allegorical figures.
A comparison with Plate XIX will show that the great astronomer was guided by
two tendencies, one of mystical and the other of national origin.*

favourable circumstances for the observation of bacterial antagonism, for an understanding of its principles and also of its therapeutic
applications, and corresponding with this new climate and these
new circumstances there was bound to arise a new phase in the
'prehistory' of antibiotics.

In 1875 the bacteriolytic properties of certain species of *penicillium* were observed by the English biologist John Tyndall,
during experiments destined to refute the theory of spontaneous
generation.[1] However, Tyndall paid only little attention to his
observation, and did not try to elucidate the mechanism of the
action which he had demonstrated.

In 1877, not long after Tyndall's observation, and even before
he had published it, similar observations were made by Pasteur
and Joubert. By culturing a colony of anthrax bacilli in a broth of
sterile urine, these scientists discovered that some airborne micro-
organisms could impede the development of the culture and even
destroy the bacilli that were being studied. Appreciating the importance of this phenomenon, they decided to experiment on
guinea-pigs, which they injected with both anthrax bacilli and
with airborne germs similar to those which they had found in their
first experiments. This was in some way an anticipation of Florey's
experiment (*see* p. 88), but since it was carried out with much
smaller resources its success was only partial. When publishing the
result of his observations and his experiments, Pasteur added a
conclusion which the 'discoverers' of penicillin were to justify
fully:

'All these facts may legitimately encourage our greatest hopes
from a therapeutic point of view.'

Unfortunately, absorbed by other problems, Pasteur could not
pursue the study of bacterial antagonism, a task tackled more or
less successfully by other scientists. The preparation by filtration
of an extract of the secretions of the bacillus *Pseudomonas pyocyanea*,
made by the German biologists Rudolph Emmerich and Oscar
Löw in 1897, marked the culminating point of this work. But
although this extract proved to be effective against various bacteria,

---

[1] These observations, made in December 1875, were, at least partially, communicated to the Royal Society in January 1876. However, a detailed description
was given only in the author's *Essays on the Floating Matter of the Air in Relation to
Putrefaction and Infection*, London, 1881.

its toxicity was such that attempts at therapeutic applications, which had aroused such premature hopes, were soon abandoned. During the entire thirty years separating the discovery of pyocyanase from that of penicillin this branch of biology was never deserted by research workers, but on the whole the advances made in it were minimal.

How can we explain the relative failure of all the efforts at consolidating the results obtained by Tyndall, Pasteur, Joubert, Emmerich and Löw? It seems that with D. Papp[1] we must see the essential reason in the imperfection of the techniques applied—especially in the purification processes, in the general lack of microbiological and chemical knowledge, and finally in the lack of co-ordination between bacteriological, chemical and clinical research. Perhaps I. B. Cohen is right, when, in his brilliant study, *Science, Servant of Man* (Boston, 1948), he points out that the definite discovery of the properties of antibiotics and their intensive use in therapy came about precisely at that moment when there was a fusion of all the knowledge required by the discovery, i.e. at the very moment when science in general was ripe for it. If taken too literally, such an interpretation might lead to underestimating the contribution of the most original scientists, but nevertheless it leads to a better understanding of the partial failure of some precursors whose efforts were paralysed less by their lack of intuition and method than by the fact that science and technique had not evolved sufficiently at that time. Since certain scientists, somewhat unfamiliar with the history of science, are still too apt to judge the work of their many precursors by simple comparison with their own, we must not overlook the fact that the value, the importance and the novelty of a discovery cannot be appreciated outside the framework of the science of the times.

(d) The Invention of Airships

A further example of invention, that of airships, will demonstrate the almost insoluble difficulties which frequently stand in the way of attempts at explaining the origins and the antecedents of a

---

[1] 'The History of Antibiotics' (*Rev. Hist Sc.*, Vol. VII, 1954).

discovery, so necessary in accounting for the logical development of the ideas which led to its realization.

In his excellent work on the history of aeronautic ideas before Montgolfier,[1] M. Jules Duhem tells of the different ways which man has sought to conquer gravitation and to raise himself into the air. If the observation of the flight of birds led Leonardo da Vinci to devote to mechanical flight much research and patient experiment, the failure of which could only be explained by modern aerodynamics, this famous example does no more than illustrate one of the aspects of the many different attempts made since oldest antiquity to solve the problem of aerial navigation. Mystical flight, magical flight, projected flight, flight by oars, mechanical flight, flight with sails, by parachute, springs, rockets, electro-magnetism, and by the effects of the element fire, of subtle air, of vacuums or of light fluids, are the fourteen different means which J. Duhem distinguished from innumerable more or less legendary accounts found in the abundant literature on so exciting a subject as the conquest of the air. We shall restrict ourselves here to relating the evolutions of only one of these means, the use of a light fluid leading to the invention of an airship which made its first public appearance in 1783, when the brothers Montgolfier carried out their famous experiments at Annonay.

Of all the procedures that we have mentioned, the use of light fluid lent itself best to technical applications. It was successful at the very moment when the state of science and of technique had sufficiently evolved for the implementation of this invention to be based on the simple application of known theoretical facts and on well-nigh perfected technical means. This remark, which actually applies to most inventions, nevertheless does not imply that the inventors of the airship contributed nothing but the art of constructing watertight balloons of large circumference, as some rivals and biased historians would have us believe. The success of this invention was so great, and the hopes which it raised were so over-optimistic, that we can understand why it aroused such bitter individual and national rivalries. A detached analysis of the circumstances and of the real significance of the discovery is hindered by the difficulty of checking a great deal of contradictory evidence

[1] J. Duhem, *Histoire des Idées Aéronautiques avant Montgolfier*, Paris, Sorlot, 1943.

and facts. However, we may here illustrate, using this example of a famous discovery, how complicated are the problems of priority.

In this particular case, while the circumstances of the first experiment made by the brothers Montgolfier may be very clearly established, and while the later stages of the invention of airships (the use of hydrogen, various improvements, the first ascents and the first aerial voyages) have been very accurately described, the origins of this invention are very much more difficult to establish. In order to give a correct historical perspective we shall begin with a brief recollection of the circumstances of the invention itself.

On the 5th June, 1783, before Members of the Assembly of the *Etats du Vivarais*, meeting at Annonay, the brothers Joseph and Etienne Montgolfier launched an airship of spherical shape with a diameter of approximately ten metres, filled with hot air. This very primitive apparatus was constructed from cloth lined with paper and sewn over a network of string, and the various parts of the envelope were simply laced through buttonholes. This imperfect airship, from which was suspended a heater preventing cooling of the hot air inside, nevertheless rose to a height of some hundreds of metres before settling more than two kilometres from its point of departure, some ten minutes later.

Actually this balloon, whose volume was about 800 cubic metres, would have been able to carry three passengers, had it been made of a sufficiently strong fabric. In any case, even in this somewhat simple form, the experiment marked an essential stage in the conquest of the air.

The attention of the public at large and the interest of scientists were immediately drawn towards these exploits, and in various countries similar attempts were made soon afterwards. The first systematic experiments that followed this demonstration were made in Paris.

The *Académie des Sciences*, which had received a verbal account of the Annonay experiments, appointed a commission, charged with enquiring into the circumstances and the importance of this discovery. At the same time a young physicist living in the capital, Charles, who was famous for his talents as an experimenter, thought of repeating the experiment but using, in place of the hot air, 'inflammable air' (i.e. hydrogen), whose low density compared with that of air had been known for some years. Money was rapidly subscribed, assuring him of the necessary financial means, and Charles, aided by two constructors, the brothers Robert, tried to solve the technical problems to be surmounted, viz. the production of hydrogen in adequate quantities (by the action of dilute sulphuric acid on iron), the manufacture of a relatively impermeable fabric to oppose the rapid diffusion of the gas, and finally the problem of inflation. All this was done under what we today would consider very primitive conditions. But nevertheless this attempt was crowned with success and on the 27th August, 1783, the airship of Charles and Robert, *Le Globe*, a hydrogen balloon of about four metres in diameter, rose from the *Champs de Mars* in the presence of a very large crowd (Plate XXII). Such an experiment was still so astonishing at that time, and the descent of the balloon at Gonesse alarmed the population of that town (Plate XXIV) to such an extent, that the government was forced to publish a proclamation relating the circumstances of the experiment and pacifying public opinion on the subject (Plate XXIB).

In the meantime the brothers Montgolfier had come to Paris to repeat their Annonay experiment before the commissioners of the *Académie des Sciences*. But bad weather destroyed the first balloon just as it was taking off, and they constructed a new one, richly ornamented and twelve metres in diameter, which, on the 19th September, 1783, successfully rose over the court of the Castle of Versailles, before an immense crowd led by the royal family, the court and the commissioners of the Academy. This airship, filled with hot air, carrying in a small basket a sheep, a cock and a canary, descended eight minutes later in the *Bois de Vaucresson*, some three kilometres from its point of departure.

In the following month Pilatre de Rozier, and soon afterwards other enthusiastic volunteers, by means of new Montgolfier balloons (with a circular gallery beneath), made experiments which attained ever greater heights reaching to more than 100 metres. These experiments having proved, against the advice of pessimists, that 'men can be raised to large heights without danger', and the king after some hesitation having given his permission, a Montgolfier balloon carrying two passengers, Pilatre de Rozier and the Marquis d'Arlandes, was launched on the first aerial voyage in history in the

Muette gardens, on the 21st November, 1783 (Plate XXIII). This attempt was successful and, after rising for twenty minutes, the two aviators descended unharmed on the *Butte aux Cailles*.

The success of this memorable experiment speeded the preparations of the physicist Charles and one of the brothers Robert to make a similar ascent with a hydrogen balloon, to which the young physicist had added many improvements after the success of his first experiment on the 27th August, viz. a valve for letting the gas escape in order to permit control of the descent; a nacelle suspended from ropework covering the balloon, ballast to facilitate the ascent, and a barometer to judge the altitude. On the 1st December the two aviators rose from the *Jardin des Tuileries*, before an immense crowd which Monge estimated as 150,000 people, and landed near *L'Isle-Adam* after a voyage of two hours during which they had reached the considerable height of 3000 metres.

The enthusiasm of the public and of most scientists then knew no bounds, the former seeing the fulfilment of hopes which men had nourished since the oldest antiquity. From being a simple object of curiosity and study, the balloon seemed to have been transformed into a new means of locomotion, similar to ships which for some considerable time had been used in crossing the seas.

Without appreciating the considerable obstacles which remained to be surmounted in making this conquest of the air more effective, it was thought that there were no greater difficulties to man's crossing the air than in maritime voyages. The future was to show the tenuous character of these hopes which, in fact, had to wait more than a century for their implementation.

Nevertheless, in the course of the following year aeronautic experiments and aerial voyages were increased and marked by the undeniable achievements of crossing the Channel by balloon, and also by the first aerial dramas. Although certain improvements, due to many important theoretical works and especially those of Meusnier, had been made, and although there had been some practical achievements, such as military observation at the battle of Fleurus in 1793, scientific experiments and measurements on the parts of Robertson (1803) and Biot and Gay-Lussac (1804), airships continued to evolve very slowly while the enthusiasm which they had excited slowly declined. The end of the last century and the first decades of the twentieth century were to see a provisional renewal of interest, and then man's greatest triumphs over the air.

However, the glory which fell on these first successful experimenters in this new field created very bitter rivalries. Although the discussions amongst the partisans of the Montgolfiers and the hydrogen balloons did not degenerate into too bitter quarrels, ardent claims of priority in the invention of the airships themselves were soon staked in various countries. Unable to analyse them all in this brief study, we shall merely illustrate the nature and tone of these attacks, of which the experiments of Montgolfier and Charles were the immediate object, by quoting the following passage from a letter addressed by the great Italian physicist Volta to the Portuguese scientist Magellan, then a refugee in London, dated the 28th September, 1783:

'. . . What do people think of flying balloons over here? They ask whether the French are not quite wrong to claim this discovery for themselves, when Cavendish, Priestley and all the physicists who followed them had proved the great lightness of inflammable air. For years I have amused myself with sending up soap bubbles filled with inflammable air. I have spoken of this jolly experiment in my notes on "Inflammable Air" in which I used them chiefly to demonstrate to the eye the lightness of this air. M. Barbier de Tinan and myself have tried to cause a bladder filled with this air to fly; but the weight of the bladder has always been too great. More than two years ago, at our meeting at Strasbourg, I proposed, as a means for succeeding in this experiment, either the use of larger vessels or making their membranes thinner, etc. And how often have I myself spoken of this at Paris, on the occasion of my experiments with M. Charles, and in full view of all his friends, with soap bubbles and others filled with air that rose and reached the top of the room so quickly that we had difficulties in following them with a candle used for illuminating them? I do not remember if you have seen me there or elsewhere making these experiments. Thus, instead of calling M. Montgolfier's experiment a discovery, we should do no more than applaud the industry with which he was the first to sew and glue together the many pieces so excellently, and to build a balloon of the required capacity. In this he has simply implemented our views in a very fortunate manner. He has a right

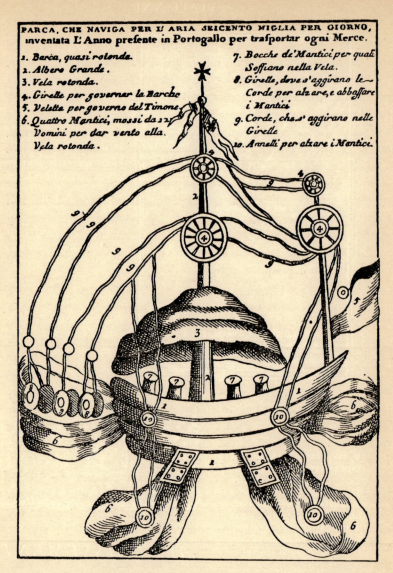

PARCA, CHE NAVIGA PER L' ARIA SEICENTO MIGLIA PER GIORNO, inventata L' Anno presente in Portogallo per trasportar ogni Merce.

1. Barca, quasi rotonda.
2. Albero Grande.
3. Vela rotonda.
4. Girelle per governar la Barche
5. Veletta per governo del Timone.
6. Quattro Mantici, mossi da 12 Vomini per dar vento alla Vela rotonda.

7. Bocche de'Mantici per quali Soffiano nella Vela.
8. Girelle, dove s'aggirano le Corde per alzare, e abbassare i Mantici
9. Corde, che s' aggirano nelle Girelle
10. Annelli per alzare i Mantici

Fig. 4.—*Fantastic design of a 'flying boat', attributed to the Portuguese inventor Lourenço de Gusmão. This rare Italian etching, dating from about 1710, is taken from 'La machine volante de Gusmão, d'après une figure comique', by J. Duhem (Thalès, vol. III, 1936, pp. 55–67).*

'A boat, travelling through the air at 600 miles per day, invented this year in Portugal for transporting any kind of merchandise whatsoever. (1) Boat, almost round; (2) Top-mast; (3) Round sail; (4) Pulleys for controlling boat; (5) Small sail controlling rudder; (6) Four bellows for blowing wind into round sail, operated by 10 men; (7) Vents through which bellows blow air; (8) Pulleys with halyards for raising and lowering the bellows; (9) Halyards; (10) Rings for raising bellows.'

PLATE XXI

A. Cyrano de Bergerac's airship as it appeared on the frontispiece of the *Fragment d'histoire comique par M. de Bergerac contenant les estats et empires du Soleil* in *Les Œuvres diverses de Monsieur Cyrano de Bergerac*, Vol. II, Amsterdam 1710

B. First page of an official proclamation explaining the nature of airships, and designed to prevent a recurrence of the incidents which took place when Charles's 'Globe' landed at Gonesse on the 27th August, 1783

'... It is intended to repeat the experiments with much larger globes. All those who notice similar globes in the sky should know that, far from being frightening phenomena, these are but machines made out of taffeta or light canvas and covered with paper, incapable of causing any ill, and probably of great benefit in the future....'

De Paris, le 27 Août 1783.

AVERTISSEMENT

AU PEUPLE,

Sur l'Enlevement des Ballons ou Globes en l'air ; celui dont il est question , a été enlevé à Paris , ledit jour 27 Août 1783 , à cinq heures du soir , au Champ de Mars.

ON a fait une découverte dont le Gouvernement juge convenable de donner connaissance , afin de prévenir les terreurs qu'elle

PLATE XXII

EXPERIENCE PHISIQUE DE LA MACHINE AREOSTATIQUE
De M. de Montgolfier Danonai en Vivarais, Repetée à Paris le 27 Aoust 1783 au Champs de Mars, avec un Balon de Taffetas enduit de Gomme Elastique de 36 pieds 6 pouces de circonference rempli d'airs Inflammable. Par M. Robert, sous la Direction de M. de Faujas de S. Fond, Et de M. Charles Profes. de Phisique. Ce Balon après avoir parcouru 4 lieues dans les airs, en 3 quarts d'heure est tombé à Gonesse.

THE FLIGHT OF THE FIRST HYDROGEN BALLOON, CHARLES'S 'GLOBE'
(27TH AUGUST, 1783)

Outside the barricades erected on the Champs de Mars a huge crowd assembled to watch the take-off.

PLATE XXIII

Premier voyage Aérien en présence de Monseigneur le Dauphin. Cette Expérience c'est faite sous la direction de M.' Montgolfier, dans le jardin de la Muette, ce Globe portant 70 pieds de hauteur sur 46 de diamettre, le poids qu'il a enlevé étoit d'environ 16 à 1700 livres, fut construit par M.' le Marquis d'Arlande et M.' Pilâtre des Rosiers, ces deux intrépides Voyageurs partirent le 21 Novembre 1783, à une heure 54 minutes après midi, ils s'éleverent à 270 pieds de hauteur, ils arriverent à bon port sur la Butte aux Cailles entre le moulin de Merveilles et le moulin Vieux, ayant vogué dans l'air un intervalle de 400 toises en 20 ou 25 minutes sans avoir éprouvé la plus legere incommodité.
A Paris chez Vachez, quai de Gevres, a l'Esperance
A.P.D.R.

THE FIRST JOURNEY BY AIR, 21ST NOVEMBER, 1783

This print shows the flight of the balloon which took off from the Muette *gardens, as seen from the terrace of the* Hotel de Franklin *in Passy. The two aviators—the Marquis d'Arlandes and Pilâtre de Rozier—were in a circular gallery made of wickerwork covered with painted canvas and suspended from the balloon. The balloon itself was richly ornamented: the top was painted with the twelve signs of the Zodiac surrounded by fleurs-de-lis, the centre bore the initials of the King between golden suns, and the bottom was painted with masks, garlands and spread-eagles which seemed to support the flight of this superb azure sphere.*

PLATE XXIV

LANDING OF THE FIRST HYDROGEN
BALLOON, CHARLES'S 'GLOBE', NEAR
GONESSE, 27TH AUGUST, 1783

The descent of the balloon greatly
alarmed the villagers. After first
exorcizing it, they made ready to cut
it into ribbons.

to recognition by physicists, and to the applause of the enthusiastic public.'[1]

Written with his tongue in his cheek, this passage shows us the nature of one of the most serious objections to the priority of the brothers Montgolfier, i.e. the claim that their invention was nothing but a repetition on a large scale of classical experiments based on very elementary principles. It cannot be denied that there is some truth in this opinion. The theoretical data of the problem were, in fact, very simple. The principle of airships is nothing but the application to the case of gases of the propositions on fluids stated by Archimedes in his treatise on floating bodies, '*De corporibus fluitantibus, libri duo*'.

But on closer examination the problem, at least in the case of Montgolfier, is a little more complex. Before analysing it in detail, a preliminary study of the case of hydrogen balloons, which Volta apparently confused with Montgolfier's hot-air balloons, will enable us to emphasize some important points.

It is certain that the experiments on the lightness of hydrogen mentioned by Volta were well known at the time, and our only criticism of the Italian physicist is that he seems to claim the idea for his own.

The discovery of hydrogen was made at least twenty years before. It was in the year 1766, in the course of his research work on gases, that the English scientist Henry Cavendish (1731–1810) managed to prepare for the first time the gas which he named inflammable air, and whose density he noticed to be very low relative to that of air.[2] And it appears that a few years later it was the English chemist and physicist Joseph Black (1728–1799) who thought of the experiment with a bladder filled with hydrogen, which Volta claims to have made. However, it is improbable that Black actually realized the experiment, for the only corroborative evidence, that of T. Thomson, in his *History of Chemistry* of 1830, must be treated with caution. Black's claims for priority in this domain cannot be considered seriously, particularly since in his view airships were mere curiosities without any value.

---

[1] After J. de Carvalho, *Correspondencia cientifica dirigado a João Jacinto de Magelhães* (*1768–1789*), Coimbre, 1952.

[2] Cavendish communicated this discovery to the Royal Society in May 1766. (Cf. *Philosoph. Transactions*, Vol. LXI, 1767.)

As regards the soap bubble experiments, Volta himself pointed out that they were mentioned in 1781 in the works of the Italian Tiberio Cavallo.[1] Cavallo, in the following year (1782), gave an account of further experiments designed to prove that hydrogen diffuses through the pores of paper much more easily than does air, and described the failure of his new attempts to raise a light vessel filled with hydrogen. The bladders he used were too heavy and his paper envelopes were too porous, and he had to content himself with experiments on soap bubbles filled with hydrogen.[2]

On the other hand experiments with balloons filled with hydrogen were carried out, in February or March of 1782, by two Italian monks of the town of Udine, who apparently succeeded in their endeavours. However, we have no precise information either on the kind of balloons they used or on the nature of the fabric of their envelope. These attempts, which went unnoticed—borne out by the fact that Volta had ignored them completely—were thus unable to influence later experiments. Is not the best proof of this the fact that the experiments of Annonay were carried out with a hot-air balloon, the brothers Montgolfier never even imagining that the use of hydrogen was possible?

Examining now the role of Charles, we shall see, and this partly confirms Volta's assertions, that the first experiments of this French physicist were a simple combination of the technical discoveries made by the brothers Montgolfier in their construction of balloons of large circumference with the large-scale production of hydrogen, the whole idea being based on the already classic experiments on the low density of this gas. However, Charles's contribution was far from being negligible; it was he who managed to produce an envelope that was impermeable enough to prevent the hydrogen from diffusing out too rapidly, and who designed and constructed most of the practical arrangements which permitted him to use the hydrogen balloon in aerial navigation.

As regards the part of the brothers Montgolfier in the invention

---

[1] *A Treatise on the Nature and Properties of Air and other permanently Elastic Fluids*, London, 1781.

[2] It should be noted that only a few weeks after Charles had managed to produce envelopes sufficiently tough for holding hydrogen, the experiment was repeated on a small scale by means of a goldbeater's skin, the outer coat of the caecum of the ox.

of airships, Volta's opinion seems to rest on a misunderstanding, since, as we stated before, he apparently confused their balloons with hydrogen balloons. Now, and this is the main point, it was on an entirely different path that the two brothers carried out their first large-scale experiments. In fact, the great experiment of Annonay was the result of a long series of observations and reflections. From 1776 to 1781 the two brothers had read and reflected on the five volumes of the French translation of the work of the English chemist Joseph Priestley (1733–1804), *Experiments and observations on different kinds of air and natural philosophy*. This treatise, which introduced them to new discoveries on 'air-like fluids', i.e. on gases, suggested to Etienne the idea that a very light and tight envelope filled with a fluid lighter than air could rise up to heights where its density would equal that of the air outside. It was the very principle of the airship which was thus suggested to him, but in a more correct form than that of the various scientists who were then experimenting on bladders filled with hydrogen.

To this purely theoretical idea were added various observations made by Joseph on the rising effect of vapour and of smoke. True, Joseph Montgolfier did not see the direct connection between these facts of observation and a law which appears so simple today, i.e. the decrease in the density of a gas when its temperature is raised. After the fashion of the times, he sought its causes in the action of some undefined fluid—perhaps electricity. It was only some months later, after the first ascensions of Montgolfier balloons in December 1783, that the Swiss physicist Benedict de Saussure gave a true explanation, exploding all theories based on the mysterious qualities of smoke.

In any case, their misunderstanding of the true causes of the rising property of hot air did not in any way hinder the brothers Montgolfier in their research and in their attempts. Joseph, who played the chief role in this invention, made his first experiments after he had observed a paper bag rising above a fire-place, and then a shirt that had become inflated above a straw fire. At Avignon he constructed a parallelepiped taffeta bag of more than one cubic metre. He burnt paper beneath it, and discovered that it rose up to the ceiling. He then repeated the experiment in the open air, where the two brothers made improvements to the shape, the fabric and the methods of constructing their primitive airship, and also increased its dimensions. Many private experiments led to an essential improvement, i.e. the addition of a heater designed to maintain the temperature of the air, and which, after trying different types of fuel, they finally fed with a mixture of wool and chopped straw. The increasing success of these attempts led them finally to try the experiment at Annonay, the first great stage in the invention of airships.

Thus the chief merit of the brothers Montgolfier seems to be the fact that they understood the principle of the airship much better than their contemporaries, that they made the correct observations, and that they had a very marked practical sense based on a profound knowledge of the physics of their time, of methods of manufacture, and of the properties of paper and sails. True, the theoretical concepts on which they originally based themselves should have led them logically to the use of hydrogen; possibly it was the difficulty of preparation and the high rate of diffusion of this gas which made them avoid the path by which Charles was to succeed. The use of hot air obviated these difficulties, but it involved the prevention of cooling, which would have caused the rapid descent of the airship. The brothers Montgolfier solved this problem by suspending a heater under the apparatus—an inconvenience of which the dangers were soon to become apparent. What reasons determined this choice? Was it the mysterious powers attached to vapours and to smoke? Or must we look for the possible influence of precursors? These are essential questions, to which it is very difficult to reply.

Besides Priestley's treatise, which according to Joseph Montgolfier's own witness had contributed greatly to the genesis of the idea of airships, it is very difficult to find other writings that might have had a decisive influence on the Montgolfiers' choice of hot air as aerostatic agent. True, the number of observers, theoreticians, dreamers and poets who have noticed and even employed the rising power of hot air was so great that it is easy to find more or less true precursors of the brothers Montgolfier, and many authors, more concerned apparently in making polemics than in going about the impartial business of the historian have, indeed, done so. This literature is so vast, so confused and so contradictory that the study of the problem has become almost impossible. Nevertheless an attentive examination of the actual documents quoted shows that they generally deal with very distant precursors.

It is very amusing to note that when a contemporary of Montgolfier, David Bourgois, tried to raise the question of priority with regard to the invention of airships, one of the brothers, Joseph, mentioned Cyrano de Bergerac as one of their precursors. The engine described by Cyrano in his *Histoire comique des Estats et Empires du Soleil* is his famous icosahedron, a large globe of hollow crystal with equal perforations at the top and at the bottom. Its facets were cut so as best to receive the sun's rays. Suspended to it was a very light box also perforated at the top and at the bottom, so that its upper orifice would fit exactly into the lower orifice of the icosahedron. A simple wooden plank served as a seat for the passenger, who controlled a sail by means of a string. The underlying principle was obviously quite fantastic: the sun, by heating the air inside, would create an ascending current of air which would raise the apparatus (Plate XXIA). There is so wide a divergence between this fantasy, and the hot-air balloon of the brothers Montgolfier, that it would be ridiculous to think that such an idea could have contributed validly to the invention of the Montgolfier balloon; perhaps the description of this fantastic engine might have induced the brothers Montgolfier to make a closer study of the rising properties of hot air, and this is surely all the credit that could be attributed to Cyrano.

Most other machines, of which there exist descriptions in the large literature of the seventeenth and eighteenth century dealing with the uses of light fluids, are just as fantastic as the icosahedron of Cyrano, and their only merit resides in their curiosity value.

As regards more positive conceptions, it seems as if the Montgolfiers had one true precursor in the Portuguese Jesuit Bartholomeu Lourenço de Gusmão (1685–1724), who, from May to October 1709, carried out a series of three experiments which, on a much reduced scale, were the forerunners of the Annonay experiment. Although Gusmão had made much more ambitious projects, and many writers and engravers had forged a quite exaggerated legend around his exploits (*see* Fig. 4), the serious, accurate and strict analysis which J. Duhem has given us of his contribution, shows clearly that this Portuguese Jesuit can be considered a precursor in a very limited sense only.

If it is incontestible that Gusmão must be cited amongst the most authentic precursors of airships, nevertheless his influence cannot be detected in what we know of the circumstances surrounding the genesis of the Montgolfiers' ideas. This, it would seem, is all that can be said about this subject, the study of which has not always been made with that impartiality and absence of passion which are so indispensable. It is regrettable that so important a question as that of the origin of airships has been examined, by most of the authors who have treated it, from the narrow considerations of quarrels of priority and national rivalries. On the part of the French, many over-enthusiastic admirers of the brothers Montgolfier made the great mistake of ignoring the existence of some precursors, and the obvious influence that the discoveries on gases had on the invention of the Montgolfier balloons. Other authors again have, by using documents of questionable value, exaggerated the possible role and importance of so-called precursors, and thus minimized the contributions of Montgolfier and the other Frenchmen who originated the great airship experiments of 1783.

Perhaps the most fruitful lesson to be learned from this rapid study is that all discoveries and all inventions of any importance are not the result of the work of one individual, but arise from combinations of many different contributions. Our attributing a discovery or of an invention to a single author is most often due to over-simplifications which explain, but do not justify, discussions of priority. A complete absence of prejudice and bias, intellectual freedom and a sharp sense of historical method are, we must stress once more, the essential mental qualities of all historians of the sciences who tackle the always delicate and complex study of the genesis of a discovery.

FORGOTTEN DISCOVERIES

(a) Mendel's Laws

There are quite a number of important scientific discoveries that remained forgotten for many years; one of the most striking examples is that of Mendel's famous principles of heredity,[1] of which we shall briefly recount the origin and unhappy fate.

Today it is well known that in 1865 the Czech monk Gregor Johann Mendel (1822–1884), assistant master at the Brno high school, published his first exact experiments on the hereditary behaviour of certain hybrid 'characters'. With very great skill Mendel had used particularly propitious experimental material in demonstrating the phenomena studied: varieties of peas that differed from one another by a small number of distinct characteristics, viz. the colour of flower or albumen, or the appearance of the seeds. Adopting a simple and strict method, he concentrated his attention on a unique characteristic and, working on a great number of samples, he studied his results statistically.

Let us briefly relate one of these experiments. After having fertilized a pea-flower with smooth seeds with the pollen of a flower with wrinkled seeds, Mendel found that all the hybrids he obtained had smooth seeds. After sowing the latter, he cross-fertilized the new plants and observed that three-quarters of the new generation had smooth seeds while the remaining quarter had wrinkled seeds. It must be noted that this last fraction gave rise to plants of wrinkled seeds, and that a study of its ensuing generations showed that this return to the characters of one of the parents is definite. On the other hand, while one-third of the smooth seeds obtained (a quarter of the total) gave rise to plants with smooth seeds in which were observed the same phenomenon of return to the original characters of one of the parents, the remaining two-thirds gave a total result similar to that which was obtained with the first lot of seeds. Later experiments confirmed that in each generation one-quarter returns to one of the initial forms, one-quarter to the other form and that the remaining half, similar in appearance to one of the parents, soon reveals its hybrid characteristics.

Studying these results attentively Mendel almost succeeded in giving a definite interpretation. He assumed that the opposing characteristics (A and A') of the two parents co-exist side by side

[1] Cf. P. Ostoya, *Les Théories de l'évolution*, Payot, Paris, 1951; C. Zirkle, 'Gregor Mendel and his Precursors' (*Isis*, Vol. 42, 1951); W. Bateson, *Mendel's Principles of Heredity*, Cambridge, 1902; H. Iltis, *Gregor Johann Mendel—Leben, Werk und Wirkung*, Berlin, 1924.

in the hybrid, but that one of these characteristics, A for example, is dominant and the only one to manifest itself. On the other hand during reproduction these pairs of antagonistic characters split, every grain of pollen or every ovule possessing either the characteristic A, or else A'. Thus each seed resulting from crossing two hybrids, or from the self-fertilization of one and the same plant, can arise from four different combinations which are equally probable:

Male A × Female A; Male A × Female A'; Male A' × Female A; Male A' × Female A'.

Thus it becomes clear that the first and the last case observed correspond to the return to one of the initial types (A for the first, A' for the last), while in the two other combinations there still exist the two opposite characters, the dominant alone being manifest.

Mendel propounded this theory, based on the result of his experiments, in a paper addressed to the Society of Natural History of Brno. But, although this paper was published in 1865,[1] and although Mendel had tried to communicate his results to many biologists of his time, his fundamental discovery did not produce any reaction, and when he died in 1884 Mendel was completely ignored by the scientific world. Nevertheless, the problems which he had studied were not without interest to some biologists, and similar experiments were made in the *Jardin de Plantes* of Paris by the French botanist Charles Naudin. However, the experimental material chosen by Naudin, i.e. different varieties of tobacco, datura and petunia, was very much less favourable than the pea, since the plants he had selected differed by characteristics depending on the many genes producing the phenomenon of mosaic characteristics, which are difficult to interpret. Thus, although Naudin had obtained results similar to those of Mendel, the complexity of facts was such that he could not find a simple and clear explanation.

[1] G. Mendel, '*Versuche über Pflanzenhybriden*' (*Verh. naturf. Ver. in Brünn Abhd.*, Vol. IV, 1865); '*Über einige aus künstlicher Befruchtung gewonnenen Hieracium Bastarde*' (*Ibid*, Vol. VIII, 1869). These articles have since been republished on several occasions.

PLATE XXV

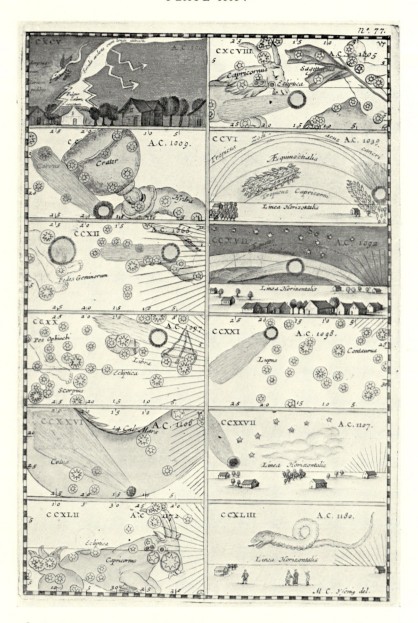

IMAGINATIVE PICTURES OF SOME COMETS THAT APPEARED BETWEEN 1000 AND 1180, FROM THE *Theatrum Cometicum* BY STANISLAV LUBIENITZ, AMSTELODAMI, 1668, VOL. II, PLATE 77

Note particularly the fiery salamander (comet of the year 1000) and the fiery serpent (comet of 1180) which, in the popular imagination, accompanied the passage of these comets. The drawings of constellations as weird figures add to the strange effect of these pictures.

PLATE XXVI

DETAIL OF BAYEUX TAPESTRY, No. 32

The left part shows a group of spectators observing Halley's Comet, which could be seen between the 22nd and 30th April, 1066: Isti mirant stella(m)—'They are star-gazing.' The raven in the foreground is an ill omen. On the right side a messenger can be seen giving news of the comet to Harold, recently crowned King of England. The boats in the foreground speak of the impending arrival of William, Duke of Normandy, who is coming to wrest the crown from Harold.

It was only in 1900 that Mendel's laws on dominant and recessive characters were rediscovered by the German biologist C. Correns and the Dutchman H. de Vries, and soon confirmed by the famous experiments of Lucien Cuénot. The bibliographical research of the Viennese biologist E. von Tschermak brought to light Mendel's paper published in 1865, and justice was finally done to the obscure monk of Brno.

Although the name of Gregor Mendel rapidly became famous and his native town raised a statue and a museum to him, some scientists were astonished that a simple amateur, who had not even managed to pass his professional examinations, working in a field which had been the object of careful research for over a century, should have managed to obtain original results of such importance. Following all clues in his papers, and examining previous publications in detail, many research workers tried to discover any possible sources of Mendel's experiments and theories. From the careful investigations of C. Zirkle[1] it would appear that Mendel must, in fact, have been familiar with the principal works published on the problem of hybrids by such indisputable precursors as Thomas Knight, Augustin Sageret, Karl von Gärtner and Johann Dzierzon. The fact that these studies and observations guided him in the choice and interpretation of the experiments can only be contested with difficulty. However, since his experiments were of far greater scope and accuracy than those of his predecessors, and in view of his clear and solid conclusions, he must nevertheless be considered as the founder of this new branch of science. C. Zirkle also spoke of a 'remarkable coincidence', which for us would seem to be an essential explanation of the origins of Mendel's discovery.

'Before Mendel, the constituent elements of Mendelism had been discovered separately, some by specialists in the hybridization of vegetables, others by agriculturalists. Very few biologists were conversant with the results that had been obtained in these two fields. Mendelism was the creation of an investigator who hybridized plants and who also raised bees.'

Thus, once more, a major discovery was the result of the combination in one and the same research work of two sources of knowledge, and of apparently independent methods and interests.

[1] *Isis*, Vol. 42, 1951.

I

Without detracting from Mendel's genius, this observation explains why so major a discovery as his famous laws could be made by a man who appeared to be so badly prepared for it.

This example of a discovery which had remained ignored despite its author's efforts is a particularly significant example of the magnitude of the obstacles which an innovator must frequently overcome. However, it must be said that there are some discoveries which were ignored owing to the wishes or the indifference of the authors themselves.

(b) Unpublished Discoveries

While the majority of research workers try to give wide publicity to those of their discoveries that appear to be sufficiently important, there are some scientists who, finding sufficient rewards for their labours in their personal satisfaction, refuse to publish some of their most important discoveries. The reasons which can lead to such an attitude are of two kinds: either a particular repugnance towards the work of writing, or the fear of having to enter into bitter polemics. It is not unnecessary to add that such disinterest is generally found in the case of 'princes of science' whose reputation is already so very solidly established that it does not depend on the publication of a new discovery.

The most typical examples of important discoveries that remained ignored because of their authors' wishes are Newton's essential contributions to optics, celestial mechanics, and the infinitesimal calculus. Newton only published these discoveries long after they were made. Cavendish's important results in electrostatics in the eighteenth century had to be rediscovered by Coulomb and Faraday; the great English physicist had preserved them in his papers, which were only explored a century later. Finally, there were Gauss's fundamental discoveries of elliptic functions and non-Euclidian geometries, which the great mathematician allowed others to rediscover without even claiming priority. It cannot be denied that such an attitude must impede the rapid progress of science, and the only valid explanation of it seems to be some sort of misanthropy on the part of these scientists.

QUARRELS ABOUT PRIORITY

The long polemics which, owing to the unfortunate intervention of over-zealous disciples, took place between Leibnitz and Newton in 1699, on the respective role of these two scientists in the discovery of the infinitesimal calculus, is both one of the most classical examples of quarrels about priority, and also one of the saddest episodes in the history of mathematics. This polemic had very unfortunate repercussions: not only was it the cause of malevolent attacks revealing very base sentiments on their authors' part, but it was also the cause of the long rupture which, till the beginnings of the nineteenth century, was to separate English from Continental analysts, thus retarding the progress of science.

Unfortunately, the history of science recalls many similar quarrels of priority. If, as in our example, a detached and objective analysis of the question will generally reveal that different discoveries of one and the same fact were made quite independently by the two adversaries, there are some other cases where the bad faith of one of the contenders is quite manifest. Charles Nicolle has devoted some scintillating remarks to what he calls 'these thieves of discoveries'.[1]

But in most cases both contenders seem to be men of unquestionable merit, and one can only regret the lack of coolness and objectivity which led them into discussions from which their prestige always emerged impaired. True, it is more often the intervention of over-enthusiastic disciples or of national vanity than the direct action of the interested scientists themselves which is the cause of such quarrels. Without insisting further on these regrettable manifestations of the vanity and exaggerated pride of some scientists, it seems necessary and useful to bring our attention to bear on their most frequent cause, viz. the simultaneous appearance of results in parallel work on problems which are of general interest during a particular period.

THE COINCIDENCE OF DISCOVERIES

There are many discoveries which are made possible by the general progress of science, and appear almost simultaneously in the

[1] *Op. cit.*

minds of different scientists. In every epoch there arises a definite predilection for particular fields, and this is favourable to such coincidences. Their relative frequency shows that even though a discovery must be attributed to its author, it belongs also and emphatically to its epoch. As examples in mathematics we shall cite the discovery of analytical geometry by Descartes and Fermat, that of infinitesimal analysis by Leibniz and Newton, that of non-Euclidian geometry by Lobatschevsky, Bolyai and Gauss, and the theory of elliptic functions, published simultaneously by Abel and Jacobi. In astronomy we shall only recall two cases mentioned elsewhere, i.e. the discovery of the satellites of Jupiter and the discovery of Neptune.

In physics, the examples are innumerable: the principle of the barometric experiment on the Puy de Dôme, the discovery of the laws of refraction, that of the principle of interference, the observation of the lines of the Solar spectrum, the inventions of the Leyden jar and of the Daniell cell, the discovery of induction, are only a few chosen at random.

This frequent convergence of the efforts of different research workers by no means reduces the personal worth of the individual. It only gives us a better understanding of the causes of the genesis of every discovery.

CHAPTER X

MISSED DISCOVERIES

WHEN studying a scientific paper with some detachment, it often happens that on a first examination one is apt to think that the work was not pursued to its limits, and that its consequences were not sufficiently exploited. Most often, however, this impression is due to a thoughtless application of modern criteria. If one tries hard enough to enter into the spirit of those times, the impression will often disappear, and it will be seen that for the desired consequences to have occurred the author would have had to make efforts for which he then lacked the necessary means. In these cases, therefore, we cannot speak of missed discoveries, but merely of the necessarily limited character of the work. On the other hand we can speak of a missed discovery when an essential fact, arising directly from his work, was overlooked by a particular scientist, or when he failed to see its significance.

The explanation of these failures is one of the essential problems confronting psychologists of invention. However, there is generally an absence of reliable witnesses, so that most explanations can only be conjectural.

THE EXAMPLES OF M. HADAMARD

M. Hadamard has been particularly interested in this problem in the domain of mathematics.[1] The examples which he quotes show the preponderant roles of too rigid an approach in research and of too logical a directing of the subconscious. Thus he relates that during his first investigations he discovered a formula which he judged as important but for which he could not perceive any immediate applications. At that time his attention, like that of many other analysts, had been drawn to the proof of Picard's theorem.

'Now my formula,' he tells us, 'evidently showed the relation between the growth of an entire function and the distribution of

[1] *The Psychology of Invention.*

its zeros, a result which, fortunately for my vanity, I was to re-discover later on another path. However, as regards the obvious fact, that all this was a very simple consequence of my unpublished formula, I was quite unaware of it, till the moment when I saw this formula over the signature of Jensen.'[1]

Many other examples cited by J. Hadamard are equally con-vincing. Thus two facts implicitly contained in his paper, but which he had failed to notice clearly, were so obvious that one of them was attributed to him later on. The same author explains equally how he just missed two fundamental discoveries, viz. that of the absolute differential calculus and that of relativity.

POINCARÉ AND THE THEORY OF RELATIVITY

The example of the theory of relativity confirms us further in the opinion that an essential discovery always comes at its proper time, at a moment when the ground for it has been prepared by research workers, and by the interest of many scientists. How-ever, this comment by no means diminishes the merit of that scientist who dares to take the decisive step, and whose part in the discovery is essential. Many first-class scientists, such as Lorentz and Henri Poincaré, had approached this fundamental discovery, but without the courage of making their thoughts explicit. This was to be Einstein's essential merit, who, in a paper of major im-portance published in 1905, resolutely took a new standpoint and created the theory of relativity, appreciating its immense sig-nificance and its great potentialities. This hypothesis, which led to a renunciation of the traditional notions of the absolute nature of space and time, assumed since Newton, demanded on its author's part a penetrating mind, profound intuition of the nature of physical reality, and an exceptional courage of mind.

Poincaré, who had so much wider a mathematical background than Einstein, then a young assistant in the Federal Patents Office of Berne, knew all the elements required for such a synthesis, of which he had felt the urgent need and for which he had laid the first foundations. Nevertheless, he did not dare to explain his thoughts, and to derive all the consequences, thus missing the

[1] *L'Invention.*

decisive step separating him from the real discovery of the principle of relativity.

In his remarks on Henri Poincaré, Louis de Broglie analyses attentively the reasons of this failure:

'Why did Poincaré fail to advance to the limits of his thought? No doubt this was due to his somewhat hypercritical turn of mind, or perhaps to the fact that he was a pure mathematician. He had a somewhat sceptical attitude towards physical theories, and thought that there was generally an infinity of different viewpoints and different ideas, all logically equivalent, from which the scientist only chooses for reasons of convenience. It appears that this nominalism caused him sometimes to misunderstand the fact that, amongst possible logical theories, there are nevertheless some which are closer to physical reality or, in any case, better adapted to the physicist's intuition, and therefore more apt to aid his efforts.'[1] Thus, in this case, the cause of the failure lay not so much in a fortuitous circumstance and a slight lack of attention, but in a much deeper layer of the mind.

THE 'FAILURES' OF PASCAL

The same is the case with some other examples quoted by J. Hadamard, who, comparing two fundamental rules of logic contained in *L'Art de Persuader* by Pascal, is astonished that the superb intellect of the author of the *Pensées* should have failed to notice that the two rules were quite contradictory, which would have led him to the notion of axiomatic definitions. Furthermore, this is not the only failure of this nature in the case of Pascal, an intuitive mind who did not always exploit with sufficient tenacity the fertile ideas which he conceived. Thus, in his various studies of the famous roulette problem, he designed a method which after some improvements permitted Leibnitz to create the infinitesimal calculus. For Pascal this method remained a simple aid to calculation, of which he did not perceive the fundamental importance.

'I do not know by what fatality,' writes Leibniz, 'Pascal failed to see the implications of his studies of infinitesimal geometry. Had he realized fully what he was doing, he would have been the creator of the algorithm of the differential calculus.'

[1] L. de Broglie, *Savants et découvertes*, Paris, Albin Michel, 1951.

And L. Brunschwicg, quoting this passage, remarks very justly that a new method can only assume its true value and its definite form at that moment when the study of new problems and the opening up of new perspectives permits its integration into science. For this to happen 'new problems deriving from prior developments must find a creative mathematician'.[1]

The above remarks would seem to justify our distinguishing in the missed 'discoveries', of which the history of science gives us so many examples, between true failures due to a simple lack of attention or to too one-sided an orientation in an author's research work, and those apparent failures the causes of which are much deeper, and which are only the necessary stages in the genesis of later discoveries.

The study of these apparent failures justly deserves to hold the attention of historians of science, since it leads to a better appreciation of some of the difficulties which should have been solved, some of the obstacles which should have been overcome, and also of the new steps in thinking which must be taken before some fundamental discoveries can be realized effectively.

AMPÈRE AND INDUCTION

Thus a history of science must do more than merely mention successful discoveries; over and beyond this it must point out some failures, the interpretation of which is often as informative as that of the most brilliant successes. In the sphere of physics such cases of 'failure' are very many and the history of induction can provide us with two particularly striking examples.

The magnificent series of discoveries which followed the announcement of Oersted's famous experiments led to the demonstration and explanation of the main phenomena produced by the magnetic effects of a current. Many physicists were interested in the problem of a possible reciprocal phenomenon, viz. whether a magnetic field could not produce an electric current flowing in a closed circuit. Their first attempts for demonstrating such a phenomenon were doomed to failure, since they were based on the wrong idea that the mere presence of a magnet would be able to

---

[1] Quoted by L. Brunschwicg in *L'Invention*.

produce a current.[1] In the meantime various experiments, made with different ends in view, had shown the existence of this phenomenon of induction, which physicists were vainly trying to detect.

The first of these experiments, made by Ampère and his friend Auguste de la Rive in Geneva at the beginning of September 1822, were soon to be repeated in Paris, where they excited the interest of physicists. But no one thought of drawing conclusions which to us seem only too immediate. The principle was very simple. A very light ring made from a thin strip of copper was suspended from a silk thread over a flat coil of wire wound parallel to the ring, and the latter was placed in the field of a powerful permanent magnet. Ampère discovered that the ring would move slightly whenever a current was set up in the coil, and that it would return to its original position once the circuit was broken.

Actually this was simply a case of the displacement in a strong magnetic field of a conductor (the copper ring) in which a current is induced by rapid changes in the flux emanating from the coil. Ampère understood this clearly, for he had also been studying the effects of attraction and repulsion between 'portions of electric current' of the same and of the opposite sense. In a letter written a few days after this experiment to his friend Bredin, he summarized his results in one sentence: 'The experiment has demonstrated the production of a current by an agency which I have unsuccessfully investigated for more than a year.'[2]

However, the circumstances under which the experiments were made were not very favourable to a more accurate interpretation. Ampère believed that, since the deviation persisted while the current was flowing in the prime circuit, the induced current, too, must needs have continued to flow, and that the return of the ring to its initial position upon breaking the circuit was due to the fact that the induced current had ceased. This erroneous interpretation, as he

[1] This idea actually contradicts the principle of the conservation of energy, for its demonstration would have involved a perpetual source of energy. We know, in fact, that a current can only be induced in a closed circuit, when there are changes in the magnetic flux cutting it. The e.m.f. of this current in volts is $e = -\frac{d\phi}{dt}$, where ϕ is the flux of the magnetic induction in maxwells. However, the very notion of the flux of magnetic induction was not understood till some twenty years later.

[2] Letter to Bredin of the 24th September, 1822. Ampère is alluding to his failure in July 1821 with a magnet that was too weak.

himself was to realize later, rested on the false hypothesis that the
suspension wire had a large coefficient of torsion.

Ampère, more than any other scientist of his time, was able to
understand the phenomena which he observed, to devise experiments which could improve his hypothesis and facilitate its study and
finally its precise interpretation. Now it must be evident that the
production of an induced current can be demonstrated simply and
much more accurately by the suppression of the permanent magnet,
and by putting a galvanometer in the induced circuit; the making
and breaking of the primary circuit would then produce sudden
deviations in one or the other sense of the galvanometer needle, a
fact which Ampère, with his gift for synthesis, could not have failed
to interpret correctly.

Having discovered a phenomenon as important as the production
of 'current by influence',[1] the study of which should apparently
have been his chief concern, why is it that Ampère neglected to make
a deeper study of it, and thus missed making a discovery which is
apparently the logical consequence of his previous work? The
reasons are very simple. Overtaxed by heavy duties, by the many
papers which he published, and by his many different experiments
to perfect and complete all his theories on electro-magnetic phenomena, and by having to counter the many objections to his work,
he could only have tackled the study of an entirely new phenomenon by giving up his other work. Furthermore, at the time,
this demonstration of the possibility of producing a current by
'influence' did not so much interest him for its immediate significance, as for its possible role in the proof of the magnetic theory
which was then one of his chief concerns. In his own words the main
reason for this lack of interest, which strikes us as somewhat paradoxical, was his obsession with settling the problem whether
magnetism was caused by molecular currents, a theory of his which
most perspicaciously anticipated modern ideas.

In a letter to Auguste de la Rive in April 1833, when he had just

[1] He himself appreciated the importance of this fact. Thus on the 25th September
he wrote to Auguste de la Rive's father: 'Your son has devoted all his time, helping
me with experiments that I could not have made unaided, or in which I had failed,
such as the production of currents by influence, which is very important when
one wishes to relate the phenomena I have studied to physical causes, and generally
to prove the existence and to calculate the forces producing them.'

become acquainted with the great discovery of induction by Faraday, Ampère regretted the fact that in 1822 they had only paid attention to one, and what is more, a negative, aspect of their experiment, thus cheating them of a discovery which was actually its logical consequence.

'It is a fact that in 1822 we were the first to obtain an electric current by "influence" or induction as M. Faraday calls it, when we set up a current in a coil surrounding a ring made of a thin strip suspended by a silk thread GH from a hook K [*see* Fig. 5]; this effect

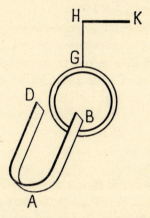

FIG. 5.—*Sketch of apparatus with which Ampère 'missed' the discovery of induction* (Correspondance du Grand Ampère, vol. II, p. 761)

showed itself through the attraction or repulsion respectively of a strong iron horseshoe magnet A [lent to us by M. Pictet], according to which pole was placed inside the ring at B. . . . Unfortunately neither you nor I dreamt of analysing this phenomena and of drawing all the conclusions. Else we should have noticed what was later discovered by M. Faraday, viz. that the current only lasts an instant, and that it flows in the opposite sense to the current set up in the coil which produces it by induction.

'It is to Faraday that we owe the discovery of all the laws of currents produced by influence, it is he who was the first to recognize that these arise not only at the moment when one sets up or interrupts the current in a coil, but also when the influence is brought closer or is removed; in such a way that when one produces the inducing current or brings it closer, the instantaneous [induced] current is in a contrary sense to that obtained when the inducing current is destroyed or else moved away.

'This is, in fact, what happened in our experiment, which, as I have assured myself since M. Faraday's discovery, was one of the most important of the century, and which has crowned the edifice others have built. His [Faraday's] completion of the theory of electro-dynamic phenomena does not alter the fact that at Geneva we together obtained a current by influence in the experiment in question.'[1]

Ampère then mentions two misconceptions on Faraday's part, which he thought of communicating to him. The English physicist apparently believed that in their experiments Ampère and La Rive had used a disc instead of a 'very thin strip bent into a circle', and he had attributed to Ampère the erroneous statement that 'the current produced by influence was in the same sense as that producing it'. In a letter to Faraday in which he asked him to be so kind as to rectify what he had written on the subject, Ampère revealed the basic reasons for his failure.

'I assure you that at the time I never once tried to find out in which sense a current is produced by induction. I had but one aim in making these experiments, and by taking a look at what I published at the time, where I described the apparatus that I used, you will see that I was only concerned with solving the question whether electric currents are due to magnetic attraction and repulsion present before magnetization in the molecules of iron, steel and two other metals, in a state which does not allow them to exercise any action outside, or whether they are produced at the moment of magnetization by the influence of neighbouring currents.'[2]

In a subsequent letter to La Rive he returns to the explanation of the experiment:

'The discoveries of M. Faraday, from which M. Nobili so brilliantly deduced the true explanation of M. Arago's experiments,[3]

---

[1] Ampère to Auguste de la Rive, April 1833. (*Correspondance du Grand Ampère*, Vol. II, Paris, Gautier-Villars, 1936.)

[2] Letter by Ampère to Faraday, 13th April, 1833. (*Correspondance*, Vol. II.)

[3] This was an experiment in 1824 directly related to the phenomenon of induction with a magnetized needle placed over a copper disc.

on the mutual action of a moving disc and of a free magnet that can turn about the same axis, equally serve to explain all the given conditions of our experiments.

'The thin strip, bent into a circle, moves towards or away from the poles of the horseshoe magnet and remains approximately in the same position while the current is flowing in the coil, precisely because the action is instantaneous, and is not present while the current continues to flow. When one stops the current, the circular strip returns to its original position because an instantaneous current is produced in the opposite sense. I attributed this returning to the force of torsion in the string, and this caused me to believe that the first action persisted while the current lasted, leading to an equilibrium with this supposed force of torsion, which does not in fact exist. As regards the direction of the current, I have never, in fact, made the necessary experiment to determine it. But it is a fact that in three or four places in my papers where I have spoken of this, I have always avoided mentioning it, because I always proposed to make a complete investigation of currents by influence, and this I have never yet done.'[1]

ARAGO'S EXPERIMENT

A second example of a similar failure can also be found in the history of the discovery of induction. In 1824 a builder of scientific precision instruments, who was famed for the quality of his apparatus, H. P. Gambey (1787–1847), noticed that the magnetized needle of a compass returned much more rapidly to the position of equilibrium when it was placed above a copper disc. Gambey used this very mysterious phenomenon to improve the construction of compasses, and being justly curious, he asked Arago to explain the cause of this rapid damping. Arago repeated this experiment in different ways and found that the rotation of the disc produced a deflection of the needle in the same sense, while in turn the rapid rotation of the latter affected the disc. Classifying these different phenomena under the name of magnetism of rotation, he believed that he could interpret them all by the hypothesis of magnetism

[1] Letter by Ampère to Auguste de la Rive, 8th November, 1833. (*Correspondance*, Vol. II.) Strangely enough, Ampère appended his letter of April 1833, previously quoted, which had been mislaid amongst his papers.

induced by the poles of the needle in a disc in close proximity. Many physicists, particularly Seebeck, Prévost, Colladon, Herschel, Babbage and Ampère were interested in this experiment, whose explanation appeared to be so unsatisfactory. Although they had obtained some results of secondary importance, the puzzle appeared insoluble, and the question seemed to have arrived at a dead end when the discovery of induction phenomena by Faraday permitted the satisfactory explanation of this phenomenon. It was in August

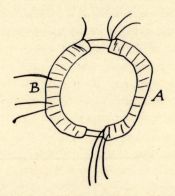

Fig. 6.—*Sketch from Faraday's notes, of the apparatus he used in discovering electromagnetic induction on the 29th August, 1831.* This was a soft iron ring, half of which was surrounded by a coil (A) connected to a battery of ten cells, and the other half by a coil (B) connected to a primitive galvanometer. Compare this sketch with Plate XVI, which is a photograph of the original ring kept in the London Science Museum.

1831 that Faraday managed to prove the existence of induced currents, but in an entirely different way. He actually used two coils mounted on the two halves of a ring of soft iron and connected the first to a battery, and the second to a rudimentary galvanometer (Fig. 6 and Plate XVI). He discovered that the closing or opening of the primary circuit produced in the secondary circuit weak currents of short duration in the opposite sense. The success of this experiment quickly led to his search for a similar explanation of Arago's experiments and he tried to demonstrate an induced current, whose existence would permit the explanation of the phenomenon which had so far remained mysterious.

'I am busy just now again on electro-magnetism,' he wrote to a friend on the 23rd September, 1831, 'and I think I have got hold of a good thing, but I cannot say. It may be a weed instead of a fish that, after all my labour, I may at last pull up. I think I now understand why metals are magnetic when they are in motion and generally not when they are at rest.'

This last sentence evidently alludes to Arago's experiment which Faraday repeated on the 28th October with some changes designed to increase the intensity of the induced currents and to permit their demonstration: he replaced the magnetized needle with a strong fixed magnet, and on the axis and the periphery of the moving disc he placed sliding contacts connected to a galvanometer. The experiment was conclusive, the rotation of the disc was accompanied by the production of a current, detected by the galvanometer. Thus Faraday, if he could not give an exact interpretation of Arago's experiment, was at least able to show the part played by induced currents. At the same time he was the first to produce a continuous current from mechanical energy by means of the first, still very rudimentary, model of an electro-magnetic machine.

In the course of the following months a brilliant series of experiments enabled Faraday to formulate the laws of induction, and Arago's experiment, which had been a mystery for so long, was slowly elucidated by the work of Faraday and Nobili. The latter, in particular, demonstrated that during one rotation of the needle, two currents arose in the two halves of the disc and were propagated symetrically along the diameter parallel to the needle, finally to reunite on this diameter in the same direction.

Thus, although many years before the discovery of induction this experiment had been a direct application of a phenomenon that no physicists could explain, it only contributed indirectly to the demonstration of this effect. In fact, although apparently very simple, it was really a very complex phenomenon, a full understanding of which involved a clear knowledge both of the laws of induction and also of the distribution of currents in a disc. In contrast to the experiment of Ampère, which could easily be adapted for the discovery of the laws of induction, Arago's inherently complex experiment made it very difficult to derive these laws directly. Furthermore, in Arago's experiment the production of currents by influence was far more difficult to demonstrate than in Ampère's experiments.

All the first investigators used a magnetized needle, and thus the intensity of the induced current was too weak to be detected by the very primitive galvanometers employed at the time. It would appear that if the reason of Ampère's failure was essentially a psychological one, in Arago's case experimental difficulties seem to have played as unfortunate a role as his false hypothesis of 'magnetism of

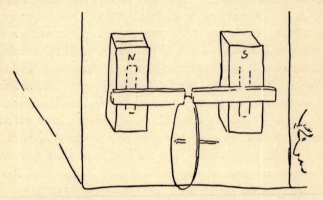

FIG. 7.—*Faraday's sketch of the apparatus with which he improved upon Arago's experiment.* A copper disc was rotated between two pieces of metal joined to the poles of a powerful magnet. The current induced by the rotation of the disc was collected by contacts on the axis and the circumference of the disc. With the success of this experiment, on the 28th October, 1831, Faraday invented the first electro-magnetic generator of continuous current.

rotation' which, in the apposite words of E. Bauer,[1] stood 'like a screen between the physicist's mind and reality'.

THE ROLE OF SPERMATOZOA

Perhaps in the biological sciences failures are even more numerous since, in evolving a new theory from a series of experiments or observations, the biologist must not only have a perfect sense of scientific procedures, but very often exceptional courage. The data which he has to consider are in fact extremely complex, and their interpretation much more delicate than is the case in the other sciences. Furthermore, philosophical conceptions, existing cheek by jowl with basic hypotheses, have long obscured ideas in

[1] E. Bauer, *L'Electromagnetisme hier et aujourd'hui*, Paris, Albin Michel, 1949.

PLATE XXVII

Figure d'vne Comette admirable veue en l'air.

COMET OF 1528 AFTER AMBROISE PARÉ

(*Les Œuvres d'Ambroise Paré*, Paris 1579, Fig. 341)

Paré gives special place in his list of 'sacred monsters' to this comet, which he has shown surrounded by swords and flamboyant masks. His meticulous drawing of these is characteristic of his work and ideas.

PLATE XXVIII

HALLEY'S COMET AS IT APPEARED IN 1910

Note how small is the head compared with the tail which is divided into two parts. The planet in the lower right of the photograph is Venus.

this field, and have often prevented an objective interpretation of observed facts. Finally, the inadequate means of observation used until very recently have frequently stood in the way of carrying out decisive experiments which alone could have determined the value of conceptions or of fundamental hypotheses. Thus many phenomena that were investigated by eminent biologists with limited experimental procedures could not be explained properly.

We shall only quote one example, that of the great Italian biologist Spallanzani, whose remarkable series of experiments actually demonstrated the role of spermatozoa in fertilization, but who failed to explain or even to understand what all his experiments ought to have suggested to him. One false experiment seems to have been the main cause of this failure. Spallanzani believed, wrongly, that he had managed to prepare a sperm free of its 'animalcule' but nevertheless still active.[1] Spallanzani was a first-class experimenter and should apparently have been able to assess his experiment critically and to see its faults. His failure is a further instance of the bad consequences of outdated ideas and of too tendentious a direction of research.[2]

MISSED INVENTIONS

In the realm of technical inventions, we must add to the causes of failure already mentioned those due to the simultaneous intervention of widely different factors. First of all there are those 'inventors' who lack the theoretical basis which alone could enable them to perfect their work or increase its efficiency. Then there are those who lack the necessary financial resources to implement or to demonstrate their discoveries. Finally, there are the many scientists who are too bent on discovering physical laws, and who do not pay sufficient attention to the practical or industrial applications of the instruments they have invented, or the phenomena that they have demonstrated. In 1854, Charles Bourseul, a modest telegraphist, managed to make the first rough design of an apparatus for the transmission of articulated sound, i.e. the telephone. However, the poor state of his theoretical knowledge, and lack of support

[1] *See also* Jean Rostand, *Les origines de la biologie expérimentale, et l'abbé Spallanzani*, Paris, Fasquelle, 1951.
[2] Plates IX, X and XI contrast the original observations of spermatozoa with the very detailed photographs recently obtained by means of ultramicroscopy.

from the administration, prevented the full development of his apparatus, which had to wait for the improvements made to it by the Americans Elisha Gray and Graham Bell in 1876.

We may be surprised at the fact that electroplating, a direct consequence of the electrolytic phenomena that had been studied since the beginning of the nineteenth century, was not applied industrially before the Russian physicist Jacobi did so in 1837. Copper deposits on the cathode had actually been noticed by many physicists, and Auguste de la Rive had described this phenomenon very accurately:

'The copper plate is coated evenly with a layer of copper in the metallic state, which is continuously deposited by the molecules; and such is the perfection of the leaf of metal formed, that when it is taken out it presents a true copy of each scratch on the metallic plate on which it appears.'[1]

This description is so clear that one may well be astonished that its author did not try to apply the observed phenomenon to industrial purposes. The main reason was certainly the fact that La Rive attached far too much importance to the theoretical aspects of the observed fact. But perhaps another factor had contributed equally to this lack of interest, viz. the absence, at that time, of generators of continuous currents other than cells.

---

[1] Quoted by E. Claparède, in *L'Invention*.

CHAPTER XI

THE STRUGGLE AGAINST ROUTINE

CERTAIN fundamental discoveries which have transformed some sectors of science have required exceptional intellectual courage on the part of their authors. In effect, these discoveries involved a complete break with apparently very solidly established opinions, with the most common preconceived ideas, and with theories considered as evident by common sense.

OBSTACLES ENCOUNTERED BY INNOVATORS

Every great discovery has produced some sort of intellectual scandal, has been opposed by current, and always badly informed, opinions on the basic nature of scientific problems, and also by the majority of scientists of the time holding outdated theories, and incapable of renouncing some of their most solidly ingrained ideas. To be just to these adversaries, who frequently opposed the spreading of new theories to the point of anger, it is only fair to note that in their initial presentation these theories often invite serious logical criticism. The innovator who reverses a theory and tries to replace it by another cannot hope to produce the most unimpeachable arguments and the most convincing demonstrations. The effort to rebuild an entire edifice, patiently constructed and consolidated by the work of many generations of scientists and by long tradition, is so immense that it is rare for one man to accomplish this transformation definitely by himself.

The number of revolutionary discoveries which came into their own, only after hard battles, is legion. In mathematics there is the existence of non-differentiable functions, the theory of transfinite numbers; in astronomy the heliocentric theory of Copernicus, the infinity of the Universe, the theory of gravitation, and the theory of relativity; in physics the mechanics of Galileo and that of Newton, the existence of the vacuum, the complex nature of white light, the velocity of light, wave theory, the kinetic theory of gases, Maxwell's formulae, electronic theory, and quantum theory; in chemistry the new chemistry of Lavoisier, the new theories of organic chemistry of Laurent and Gehrardt, and atomic theory; in biology the circulation of the blood, vaccination, the theory of evolution, Pasteur's ideas, etc.

Religious or philosophic dogma and political censure have played a considerable role in the battle against discoveries and new theories. The combined influence of rigid interpretations of Aristotelian and religious dogma, in particular, explains the very hard battles waged, especially in the sixteenth and seventeenth centuries, by the partisans of modern science, before they were allowed to express their points of view freely. The examples of Giordano Bruno and of Galileo show us to what point such persecutions could go, and prove that science cannot develop properly if scientists lack complete freedom of thought and expression. All forms of subservient thought are harmful to scientific progress.

However, it is an unfortunate fact, the importance of which cannot be neglected, that the hostility from other scientists met by many discoverers has sometimes been extremely brutal and quite unjustified. In the difficult struggles which many innovators had to wage for their ideas to triumph, it is very sad to note that their most rabid foes were often recruited from the ranks of those who ought to have been their firmest supporters. In this respect routine and conformity are the worst enemies of scientific progress. Experience proves that it is always dangerous to confer too much power of criticism upon even the most eminent scientists, for there are some who, with age, turn theories into unassailable dogma against which they allow no criticism. And, if their powers are too wide, some of them may reduce their young adversaries to utter silence and thus brake the progress of science. Jean-Baptiste Dumas and Marcelin Berthelot were two eminent scientists who for a time enforced a scientific dogmatism against which it was very difficult to struggle.

If, by its power, truth will always triumph over routine, dogma and prejudices, it is regrettable that such struggles should be necessary at all.

COMETS, NOVAE AND SUNSPOTS

Quite apart from conceptions of the structure of the Universe or the Solar system, the history of which is well known, the precise understanding of other astronomical facts also has been held up, because to a greater or lesser extent they ran counter to the body of generally held theories. This, for instance, happened in the cases of the periodic return of the comets, the discovery of variable stars, and of sunspots.

Observations on some large comets had been made since oldest antiquity and the relative rarity, the apparent absence of regularity, and the very curious appearance of this phenomena had aroused curiosity and even anxiety. Thus the famous Roman philosopher and statesman Seneca wrote the following:

'Whenever one of these fires, rare and unusual in form, appears in the sky, everybody wants to know what it is, forgets the other celestial bodies, is only interested in the intruder, and ignores what he should admire or fear. There is in fact no shortage of people who spread alarm and affirm the questionable significance of this phenomenon. One is overwhelmed with questions whether it is a marvel or a celestial object.'[1]

After exposing and refuting previous theories, often with a great deal of critical sense, Seneca calls attention to the lack of exact observations on the progress of comets, and affirms his faith in a future elucidation of these phenomena, that had until then remained so very mysterious:

'There will come a time when attentive study pursued for centuries will throw light on these phenomena of nature. Supposing that [nature] would reveal herself fully to a study of the heavens, one single life would still not suffice for so vast a research, and we should divide what is but too short a span of years between study and error. Furthermore to solve all these problems one would need a long succession of workers. The time will come when our descendants will be astonished that we should have ignored such obvious matters. . . . The day will come when someone will explain in what regions comets travel, why they differ so much from other stars, what is their magnitude and their nature. Let us be satisfied with

[1] Seneca, *Of Nature*, Book VII, Ch. 1.

what has already been discovered, and let us allow our descendants also to contribute to our knowledge of truth.'[1]

We may be astonished that the predictions of this beautiful declaration of faith in the explanatory value of science took so long to come true. Admittedly, the impossibility of observing it continuously, made the motion of a comet much more difficult to study and to explain than that of a planet, and thus it is not surprising that almost a whole century had to pass before Newton tried to apply to these stars the laws of planetary motion discovered by Kepler. On the other hand, it is difficult to understand why those observers who had noticed the appearance of new comets had not, before the end of the fifteenth century, attempted to study their motions. It was only in 1472 that Regiomantanus thought of following the displacement of a very bright comet which had just appeared, and then determined its successive positions. The stage was then set, and even if they failed to give a correct interpretation, most astronomers of the sixteenth and seventeenth centuries studied the path of some comets very accurately, and their observations gave them some precise examples by which to test the validity of Newton's theory.

But how can we explain the relatively late date of such observations? A lack of observational instruments could not have been responsible, since, when they were observed, most of the comets were of considerable apparent dimensions. The explanation must be sought in philosophical considerations. Aristotelian theories had been holding sway for so long that no one dared to question their correctness. Now, for Aristotle comets were not celestial bodies, but simply luminous phenomena produced in the interior of the sub-lunar world, when certain conditions led to the air being mixed with a dry and hot emanation, viz. a kind of smoke rising from the dry earth heated by the sun. It was therefore nothing but a meteorological phenomenon, appearing quite unpredictably in the neighbourhood of the earth, and connected with a special meteorological state heralding winds and dryness. One can understand that such a conception must have impeded considerably the progress of knowledge in this field. Since comets were considered as phenomena influencing the weather and even the life of the people, and not as

[1] *Ibid.*, Ch. 25.

celestial objects that were somehow related to other bodies, astronomers neglected to observe them or to calculate their motions.[1] However, when those astronomers, who were more or less aware of the weaknesses of Aristotle's cosmology, started to make careful observations, it became obvious that comets were not atmospheric meteors but heavenly bodies with unquestionably regular motions. Kepler vainly tried to relate them to his theory; his attempts were foiled by the lack of observational data and by the considerable perturbations which affected the theoretical regularity of the motion of comets. The magnificent confirmation of Newton's theory, provided by the return of Halley's Comet in 1759, was, it must be recalled, due to very fortunate factors. Of the 544 different comets that could be distinguished in 1953 there are actually no more than 44 whose periodic return has been able to be predicted to date.[2]

There is a second category of celestial objects, the observation of which was equally neglected or misunderstood because of Aristotle's cosmological teaching, viz. variable stars and especially novae, whose sudden increase in brightness is followed by a progressive weakening, returning them to their initial state. Such variations in brightness are evidently incompatible with the doctrine of the incorruptibility of the heavens. According to Pliny it was the appearance of such a nova which decided Hipparch, the great astronomer of the second century B.C., to compile his famous catalogue of stars. However, for a very long time no further observations on this subject are mentioned. It was only in 1572 that the great Danish astronomer Tycho Brahe observed accurately the successive variations in brightness and form of a nova; the small volume, *De Nova Stella*, which he published on that occasion marks the veritable entry of these bodies into science. Tycho Brahe was not afraid of asserting that the observed nova was beyond Saturn, i.e. in a zone which Aristotelian cosmology considered as immutable and

[1] Plates XXV, XXVI and XXVII are some examples of the fantastic interpretations of the appearance of comets. While the passage of the Halley Comet in 1066 was quite soberly represented by the designers of the Bayeux tapestries (Plate XXVI), the interpretations by Stanislav de Lubienitz in his *Theatrum Cometicum*, 1668 (Plate XXV), and those quoted by Ambroise Paré in his *Oeuvres*, 1579 (Plate XXVII), show a fertile imagination divorced from either observations or facts.

[2] The photograph of the Halley Comet, taken during its last passage in 1910 (Plate XXVIII), shows how far the old and fantastic conceptions (Plates XXV, XXVI, and XXVII) were removed from reality.

incorruptible. When, in 1604, Galileo observed a nova in the con-stellation of Ophiuchus, he made daring hypotheses on this subject in the course of three lectures at the University of Padua, which produced a veritable scandal amongst the partisans of Aristotelian cosmology. Although these hypotheses were largely false, they nevertheless had the great merit of demonstrating the celestial characteristics of a phenomenon that has had to await recent advances in astrophysics for its true explanation.

Some years after his observation of the nova in Ophiuchus, Galileo was to demonstrate another phenomenon whose disagree-ment with Aristotelian cosmology was even more obvious. This was the case of sunspots, whose existence abolished the doctrine of the incorruptibility of the Sun. It seems that in the observation of this phenomenon Galileo had been anticipated by the Dutch astronomer David Fabricius, and if the Jesuit Christoph Scheiner also claims priority, Galileo must at least be given credit for guessing its true nature, i.e. accidents on the Solar surface, and for appreciating the full philosophic importance of this discovery. Thus in 1612 he wrote in a letter:

'I presume that these innovations will be the funeral and the finish of, or the last judgement on, pseudo-philosophy; signs of it have already appeared in the Moon and in the Sun. I am expecting to hear of great proclamations on this subject by the peripatetics who will wish to preserve the immortality of the heavens. I do not know how it can be saved and preserved.'

This opinion of Galileo was both just and courageous; the discovery of solar spots definitely overthrew the belief in the incorruptibility of celestial matter, and thus an essential part of Aristotle's cosmology. This cosmology must furthermore be blamed for the late recognition of a phenomenon, which under favourable circumstances had already been observed on many occasions with the naked eye in the Far East and also in Russia and the West, without having been interpreted correctly.[1] But perhaps what Galileo did not foresee at that time was the obstinacy with which the partisans of these ancient doctrines were to fight him

[1] Cf. G. Sarton, 'Early observations of the sun-spots?' (*Isis*, Vol. 37, 1947); J. Schove: 'Sun-spots, Aurorae and Blood Rain; The Spectrum of Time' (*Isis*, Vol. 42, 1951).

PLATE XXIX

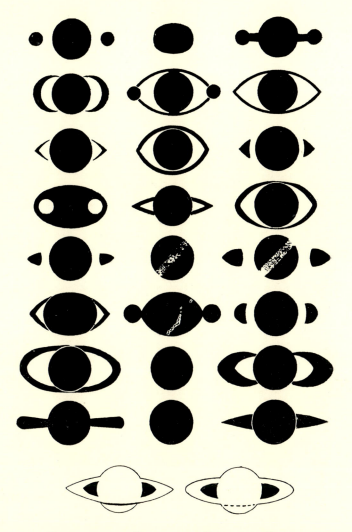

OBSERVATIONS OF SATURN FROM GALILEO TO HUYGENS

This series of 26 figures, after M. Beima (De Annulo Saturni,
Lugdunum Batavarum, *1842*) *and D. Shapley* (Pre-Huygenian Observations of Saturn's Rings, Isis *vol. 40, 1949, pp. 12–17*) *shows the chief
observations of Saturn from Galileo (1610–1612) to Huygens (1655–1656).
The first observations on the top line are Galileo's; the five on the two
lower lines are Huygen's; the intermediate observations are those of different
astronomers including Ch. Scheiner, F. Fontana, P. Gassendi, G. B.
Riccioli, F. M. Grimaldi, D. Bartoli, and J. Hevelius. While some of the
figures can be explained by the presence of the ring, others bear little
relationship to reality. See Plates XXX and XXXI.*

PLATE XXX

THIS SERIES OF FIVE EXCELLENT PHOTOGRAPHS OF SATURN, OBTAINED BY
B. LYOT AT THE PIC DU MIDI OBSERVATORY, SHOWS SOME OF THE CHIEF
ASPECTS OF SATURN

The plates explain why observers before Huygens (see Plate XXIX) were unable to give a correct interpretation. The rings of Saturn are very thin (5 km.) compared with their diameter (280,000 km.). Because the rings have an invariable inclination, their phases have a periodicity depending on the orbital revolution of Saturn in relation to that of the Earth.

PLATE XXXI

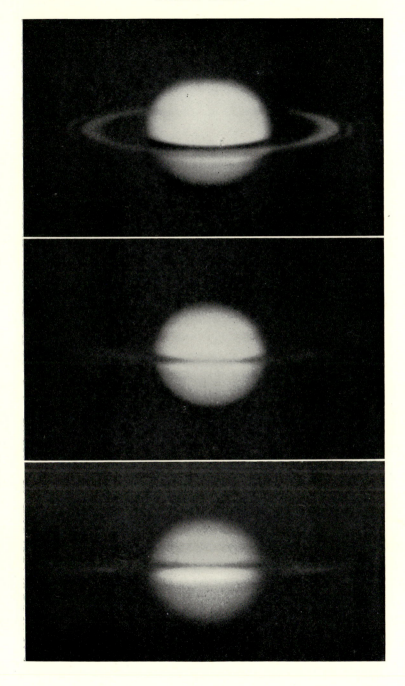

PLATE XXXII

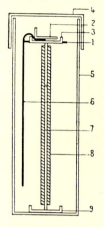

A. APPARATUS FOR ONE-DIMENSIONAL
CHROMATOGRAPHY

1, Steel protection wire. 2, Curved glass rod. 3, Petri-dish cover. 4, Cylindrical lid. 5, Glass cylinder. 6, Strip of paper. 7, Glass rod. 8, Cotton. 9, Petri-dish cover.

This diagram, and also the following photograph, are from an article by P. Boulanger and G. Biserte: 'La chromatographie de partage', in M. Polonovski's Exposés annuels de Biochimie médicale, *11th year, 1950. (Masson et Cie, Paris.)*

B. ONE-DIMENSIONAL CHROMA-
TOGRAPHY OF VARIOUS AMINO-
ACIDS

The phenol solvent system is used (NH₃ . 3%). The technique of this method of analysis is very simple. Drops of the substance to be analysed are placed on the circles printed on top of the paper strip. When the solution has evaporated, the paper strip is placed in the apparatus whose reservoir (3, above) has been filled with a water-saturated solvent. The paper is removed when the solvent has reached the desired position on it and is dried. The separated substances are detected by means of suitable reagents.

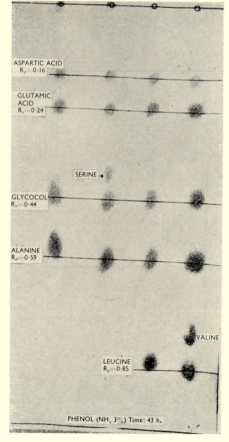

when, unable to rehabilitate their outdated doctrines, they forced him to make a humiliating recantation.

But the times had passed when such dogmatic interventions could arrest the progress of science for good. The rich harvest of discoveries that followed the widespread use of the astronomical telescope led to decisive proofs against the ancient theories, and no amount of condemnations of Galileo could uphold them against the imperative law of fact.

THE MARTYRDOM OF SEMMELWEISS

One of the saddest examples of a scientist falling a victim to his own discovery is that of the Hungarian physician Ignaz-Philipp Semmelweiss (1818–1865), who, after having discovered the cause of puerperal infection, tried, but unfortunately without success, to introduce the general use of antiseptics. The factors surrounding his discovery give a clear illustration of his scientific rigour, and thus merit our attention.[1]

In the middle of the nineteenth century puerperal fever was so rampant in maternity hospitals that women in labour were truly terrified. At the time speculations on its causes were fantastic rather than scientific; we need but mention the assumed influence of some foodstuffs and even of scents. During the autopsy of a laboratory assistant, who had died of an infection that he had contracted during a dissection, Semmelweiss noticed that some anatomical and pathological symptoms were similar to those observed in women who had died of puerperal fever. From this he concluded that both diseases had similar origins, and he was confirmed in this idea by his discovery that deaths from puerperal fever were much more common in clinics where students did their obstetrics without taking any of the precautions that today are a matter of routine. He immediately communicated his observations and ideas to the Medical Council of Vienna, and stated that puerperal fever was due to blood poisoning caused by the absence of antiseptic precautions. The rapid drop in mortality which followed upon the implementation of his advice that all who came into contact with women

---

[1] Cf. Castiglioni, *Histoire de la médecine*, Payot, Paris, 1931; F. G. Slaughter, *Immortal Magyar, Semmelweiss, Conqueror of Childbed Fever*, N.Y., H. Schuman, 1950. (*The Life of Science Library.*)

in labour should take care to wash their hands, and that wards should be disinfected by chlorination, was a remarkable justification of Semmelweiss's point of view.

However, the leading obstetricians of Vienna fought so bitterly against this thesis that Semmelweiss had to leave the hospital where he practised. In 1855 he was appointed professor at the University of Budapest, where he continued propounding his ideas. In 1861 he published his *On the etiology, the pathology, and the prophylaxis of puerperal fever*, in which these ideas were developed further and based on new observations. Refusing to accept clearly established facts, his adversaries redoubled the violence of their attacks to such a point that Semmelweiss had to abandon his Chair. Broken by such obstinacy and by the most vicious abuse, the Hungarian doctor some years later died a sad death in a lunatic asylum.

However, the work of Pasteur and the unquestionable triumph of the great English surgeon, Joseph Lister (1827–1912), slowly overcame the obstinacy of those who opposed antisepsis in the prevention of infectious diseases, and some twenty years later the correctness of the ideas of Semmelweiss was finally recognized and antiseptic methods were applied successfully to the prevention of puerperal fever. The statue that the city of Budapest erected in 1894 in honour of the great Hungarian physician, pioneer and genius, and martyr to his own discovery, unfortunately does not erase the memory of his tragic death, and of the thousands of innocent victims who had to pay with their lives for the blind obstinacy of orthodox medicine of the time. No other example seems to be as tragic as this one.

CHAPTER XII

SCIENTIFIC DISCOVERY AS THE REFLECTION OF THE CIVILIZATION OF AN EPOCH

THE CONTINUOUS PROGRESS OF SCIENCE

If so far we have insisted on the individual aspect of discoveries, nevertheless many of our examples have brought out the part played by collective factors. While some innovators had to fight against the more or less open hostility of some of their contemporaries, in most cases a scientist is rewarded for his efforts, if not materially, then at least intellectually by the renown which his discoveries bring him. Thus his work benefits from valuable incentives which, coupled with his love for science, enable him to face the long periods of unrewarding work which precede or follow a discovery.

But above everything else, it is the assistance of all those scientists who have worked in his particular field before him, and who have supplied the basis and the procedure, which will enable him to make progress. Our study of the problem of precursors has clearly shown that most discoveries were made on soil that had already been prepared to some extent, and that however revolutionary a scientist may have been, his work is only a more or less direct continuation of the work of his predecessors. In this respect science appears as a beautiful example of the collective work of men of all times and all countries.

TECHNICAL AND SCIENTIFIC LEVEL

The importance of instruments in observation and experiment is such that the technical level has direct repercussions on that of the experimental sciences, and the latter in turn is reflected in the theoretical sciences and thence in mathematics. The reverse process also is equally clear. Thus the levels attained in the three fields of scientific knowledge are always more or less interdependent, their interrelations being largely determined by political and economic factors. This fact is so well known that we need not insist on it.

THE DISCOVERY OF THE RING OF SATURN

The history of the discovery of the ring of Saturn is a typical illustration of a discovery made at the very moment when experimental techniques were ripe for it.

In 1610 Galileo began his systematic exploration of the sky, and thanks to the telescope that he had built, discoveries succeeded one another with astonishing rapidity. His *Sidereus Nuncius*, in which he describes his first observations, reflects his justifiable enthusiasm in having discovered so many marvels that had previously been unknown. Turning his still very imperfect telescope of very weak magnification towards Saturn, he observed a celestial object whose queer shape he thought was due to two very large satellites. In order to arouse the curiosity of his readers he announced his discovery by means of an anagram:[1]

SMAISMRMILMEPOETALEVMIBVNENVGTTAVIRAS

Kepler tried vainly to decipher this puzzle, and some time later Galileo himself gave the solution:

ALTISSIMVM PLANETAM TERGEMINVM OBSERVAVI
[I have observed that the furthest planet (Saturn) is a triplet].

But in fact this curious and changeable appearance of Saturn is not due to two satellites, but to the rings surrounding this planet.[2] Galileo's imperfect telescope failed him in the observation.

Galileo's discoveries having aroused a great deal of curiosity and very justifiable interest, many scientists possessing similar telescopes tried to imitate him in his attempts at extending the field of astronomical discoveries and at improving the methods. Thus in the ensuing years innumerable amateur astronomers observed and tried to explain the changeable appearance of Saturn. If Galileo's interpretation apparently failed to account for some of the observed appearances, other hypotheses, made in its stead, lent themselves to similar criticism.[3]

[1] Cf. p. 50.
[2] *See also* Boquet, *Histoire de l'Astronomie*, Payot, Paris, 1925; D. Shapley, 'Pre-Huygenian Observations of Saturn's Ring' (*Isis*, Vol. 40, 1949).
[3] Cf. Plate XXIX, which shows the principal observations of Saturn from Galileo to Huygens.

However, in 1655, the young Christian Huygens, then 26 years old, managed to construct a telescope that was much better than all previous ones. Although the observations of Saturn, which he made between the 23rd March and the 13th June, 1655 with his new instrument, were much more accurate than those of his predecessors, still the particular form of the rings at that time caused him to fail in interpreting them correctly. After constructing an even more powerful telescope equipped with a famous Huygens eyepiece, specially invented for this occasion, he resumed his observations and in March 1656 he discovered the first of the known satellites of the planet—known as Titan from then on—and in October 1656, at a moment when the rings again became visible[1] after a period of absence, he finally managed to give a correct interpretation of them. But, like Galileo, it was by means of a practically undecipherable anagram that the Dutch scientist announced this discovery in his *De Saturni Luna Observation Nova*, published in 1656:

AAAAAAA CCCCC D EEEEE G H IIIIIII LLLL MM NNNNNNNNN OOOO Q RR S TTTTT UUUUU

Only three years later, in his great work, *Systema Saturnium, sive de causis mirandorum Saturni phoenomenon*, he gave the key to this riddle:

ANNULO CINGITUR, TENUI, PLANO, NUSQUAM COHÆRENTE, AD ECLIPTICAM INCLINATO
(A thin ring, plane, without adherence, inclined to the ecliptic).

Thus despite the great number of careful observations on the part of many astronomers, most of whose work was beyond question, and despite their ingenious attempts at interpretation, a long interval of almost fifty years separates the first observation of the ring of Saturn by Galileo from its correct interpretation by Huygens. And yet the configuration formed by Saturn and its system of rings is relatively simple, at least on a first approximation. In fact it is an almost spherical planet surrounded by a vast crown, whose very small thickness (of the order 5 kilometres compared with an external

---

[1] These apparent periodic disappearances of the ring of Saturn occur when the Sun and the earth are approximately in their plane. Because of the small thickness of the ring (of the order of 5 km.) it can, in fact, not be seen 'edge on'.

diameter of some 280,000 kilometres) is negligible in the case of observers with instruments of small power. The plane of the ring coinciding with the equatorial plane of the central planet makes an angle of 27° with the plane of the orbit, and does not change during the revolution of the planet. Owing to this, and also to the combined effects of the variation of the angle of incidence of the Solar rays and the shifts in perspective due to the planet's displacement relative to the earth, its appearance changes very considerably, from the classical picture that is found in elementary textbooks to the less common one in which the ring, seen end on, seems to have disappeared. This is due to a phase phenomenon similar to that of the moon, but far more baffling, since there is no other example of it.[1]

Thus it is easily understood why an interpretation that strikes us as so simple, eluded seventeenth-century astronomers, who evidently had no precedent by which to explain it. It is also clear that the main reason of this delay must be attributed to the fact that observational instruments before Huygens were too imperfect and too weak to give the astronomers an accurate and clear enough image to put them on the right path. Before we can interpret a phenomenon correctly we must in fact be able to understand it, particularly when we are dealing with a unique case such as the ring of Saturn. Huygens has probably drawn the most important lesson from his discovery when he writes:

'Had previous observers used larger telescopes with better lenses, there is no doubt that instead of the three round bodies, they would have seen the same thing that I did in 1655, and again on the 30th October of the following year.'[2]

Nevertheless Huygens' contribution was more than that of a simple conscientious observer. Not only was he courageous enough to give the correct explanation of the observed phenomenon, but he also predicted with a good approximation the moment when the ring of Saturn would again become invisible. The confirmation of his prognostication reduced to silence those who opposed his theory, which, it is interesting to note, gave a further confirmation of the correctness of the heliocentric theory.

---

[1] The excellent photographs of Saturn obtained by B. Lyot at the Pic du Midi Observatory (Plates XXX and XXXI) give a very clear idea of this phenomenon.
[2] 'Systema Saturnium' (Œuvres, Vol. XV).

THE MATURITY OF A DISCOVERY

A number of our previous examples, particularly airships, antibiotics and spectral analysis, have clearly shown that many discoveries have appeared at that moment when they were sufficiently ripe for it.

A discovery can be considered as premature, if the level of science as a whole fails to lead to its satisfactory explanation or to the derivation of useful conclusions from it. For instance this was the case in 1675 with the Abbé Picard's observation of the luminous spots appearing in the 'empty' space of a mercury barometer when transported at night. For this phenomenon, connected with electric discharge in rarefied gases, to be understood and interpreted correctly, a prior knowledge of electrical theories and of the structure of gases was essential. Thus this discovery, although it had fruitful repercussions in the many experiments to which it gave rise, did not effectively become a part of scientific knowledge until the second half of the nineteenth century.

Similarly, in the experimental field, a new technique does not assume its true importance, and does not enter into science proper, until such time as science as a whole has attained a level at which the new method can be applied fruitfully. A recent technique of qualitative analysis, i.e. chromatography, will give us a convincing example.

CHROMATOGRAPHY

In bestowing the 1952 Nobel prize for chemistry to two English scientists, A. J. P. Martin, director of the Physico-chemical Department of the National Institute of Medical Research in London, and R. L. Synge, a biochemist at the Rowett Research Institute, the Academy of Science of Stockholm showed its appreciation of the importance of a recently perfected laboratory technique, namely, chromatography, a new method of analysis that is easily applied and extremely sensitive.

Its principle is very simple: complex substances, carried along by means of suitable liquids, are separated when these solvents are passed through an adsorption column, i.e. a glass tube containing a column of adsorbing powder (column chromatography) or a paper-filter (paper chromatography) (Plate XXXIIA and B). Although the general application of chromatographic methods to the analysis of very complex organic compounds and subsequently to the field of mineral chemistry is very recent, they are derived from the work of many research workers during the last fifty years, the foremost of which were Martin and Synge. Obviously so simple a procedure could not have remained unknown until our time; every time a schoolboy looks at the many rings on a piece of blotting paper around an inkspot, he has in fact unwittingly performed an experiment in chromatography.

Thus, when the first achievements had drawn the attention of research workers to this method of analysis, very old accounts of the use of this procedure were brought to light. In fact, it seems that it was re-invented on several occasions.

Thus in 1850, more than a century ago, the chemist F. F. Runge had analysed mixtures of dyes by means of a strip of blotting paper whose ends were dipped into the liquid to be studied. This scientist devised many similar procedures, and suggested that substances dissolved in a liquid could be separated by means of blocks of wood soaking in the solution.

Some years later, in 1861, the chemist Schoenbein also used a still rudimentary method of paper chromatography for the separation of metallic salts contained in a solution. The end of the nineteenth century knew of similar attempts which, no doubt owing to imperfections, were not as successful as they could have been.

In 1901 the Russian biologist Michael Tswett (1872–1920) made the first chromatographic analysis of the chlorophyll in an extract of green leaves. He boiled the leaves in ether over a column of finely pulverized calcium carbonate, and thus apparently rediscovered the principles of this method of analysis. In any case, it was he who proved its fruitfulness when he managed to dissociate the principal constituents of chlorophyll. However, since it was published in an obscure Russian botanical journal, Tswett's paper was ignored till 1931 when other research workers had to rediscover chromatography in a new attempt to separate similar organic substances.[1]

[1] The Academy of Sciences of the U.S.S.R. has recently collected the most important of Tswett's writings: *M. S. Tswett, Chromatographic adsorption analysis. Selected Papers* edited by A. A. Richter and T. A. Krassnosselskaja, 1946.

This happened when three investigators, Kuhn, Winterstein and Lederer, managed to separate, by chromatographic analysis in a column of porous matter, the constituents of some varieties of pigments of very similar compositions and properties, i.e. the carotenoids. Their successful analysis showed that by means of chromatography one could separate and obtain in the pure state products of very similar properties, difficult to separate by all previously known methods. Many chemists and biologists tried to apply this method to the analysis of different organic products. Once the path was opened, methods were greatly improved by means of new adsorbents and carefully chosen solvents, by the introduction of chromatography by fractional elution (the successive use of many solvents; Reichstein, 1936), improvements in paper chromatography, by the demonstration of two-dimensional chromatography (Leisegang, 1943), of divisional chromatography (realized by Martin and Synge during their research work on the amino-acids in wool, in 1941), of radio-chromatography (the use of radioactive isotopes), of electrochromatography (which, by employing an electrical field, allows a continuous operation), of gas chromatography, etc.[1]

The results so far obtained with this new method are so accurate and so striking that chromatography may be considered one of the most decisive discoveries of the twentieth century in the field of chemical analysis. We may justly hope that in the near future this method will lead to new essential advances in biology and in mineral analysis. The preparation of rare earths in the pure state, the separation and the quantitative analysis of the amino-acids, the discovery of the structure of insulin, the identification of a new hormone in the thyroid gland, are but a few of the discoveries made by means of chromatographic methods. They are, indeed, promising signs of further triumphs of a technique which is both accurate and sensitive.

Thus a method so elementary in its principle as chromatography had to wait until very recently for its fruitful application. Yet all that was needed for its discovery was that the attention of observers be directed at a common phenomenon of a strange nature. It is extremely probable that besides the few examples that we have cited, a systematic investigation will bring to light a great number

[1] Cf. L. Zechmeister, *Progress in chromatography, 1938–1947*, London, 1951.

of research workers who have studied chromatography with varying degrees of care. All that we can state definitely is that the first great success of chromatography was the separation of the constituents of chlorophyll achieved by Tswett in 1901.

This belated success can be very easily explained. The most immediate field for applying chromatography is the separation of very complex organic substances. Now, such a separation could only have become of true importance when the progress of organic chemistry, and of biological chemistry in particular, had led to the identification and the study of these very complex constituents. Furthermore, the impossibility of explaining in simple terms a phenomenon which even today is not fully understood must have enjoined great prudence. It is partially because of these reasons that a method, based on a phenomenon that had long been known, had to wait for its full development until such time as the level of chemical knowledge justified its use. We may say that this discovery was the collective work of all those scientists who knew how to derive an exact and perfect technique from a commonplace observation.

CONCLUSION

The last example has drawn our attention to the increasingly collective character of modern scientific research. The social, economic and technical reasons which have caused this development are so strong that it seems unlikely they will be arrested.

Nevertheless, if this state of affairs has the unquestionable advantages of greater technical facilities, a readier access to books, and the co-operation of research workers with complementary specialities, it also carries with it some dangers which it is important to note.

The growing role played by politics in the material and administrative organization of scientific research may well lead to a decrease of purely disinterested research work, in favour of an immediately profitable approach. The actual orientation of French scientific research does not seem to render this danger imminent, but the risk is too grave to be ignored.

The second risk which is run by the collective and administrative organization of scientific research is that of reducing individual initiative. While rational team work allows the systematic exploitation of some results, or the improvement of some new techniques, it must be stressed that fundamental discoveries arise only from the original efforts of a scientist, free to follow any fruitful paths suggested by his intuition.

Only by respecting the original qualities of each worthwhile research worker, only by heeding all the many factors that influence the work of scientific creation, can the collective organization of scientific research lead to the harmonious and fruitful development of science as a whole.

INDEX OF SUBJECTS

INDEX OF NAMES